HOUGHTON MIFFLIN

Math

MATHEMATICS

Program Authors
Harry Bohan
Gerlena Clark
Heather J. Kelleher
Charles S. Thompson

Contributing Authors
Nadine S. Bezuk
Jean M. Shaw
Lucia Vega-Garcia

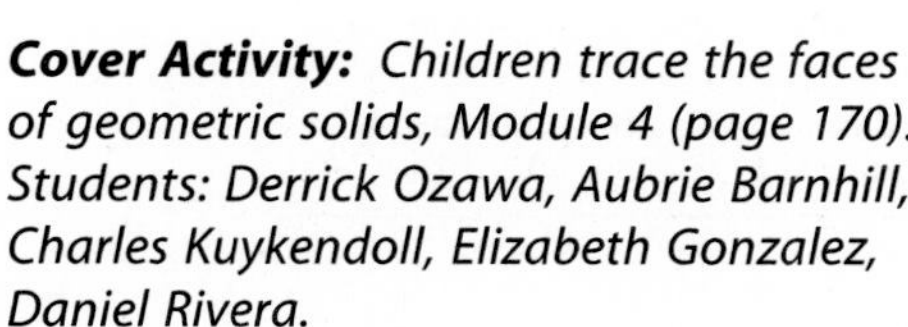

Cover Activity: *Children trace the faces of geometric solids, Module 4 (page 170). Students: Derrick Ozawa, Aubrie Barnhill, Charles Kuykendoll, Elizabeth Gonzalez, Daniel Rivera.*

Houghton Mifflin Company• Boston

Atlanta • Dallas • Geneva, Illinois • Princeton, New Jersey • Palo Alto • Toronto

Authors and Contributors

Nadine S. Bezuk
Associate Professor of Mathematics Education
San Diego State University
San Diego, CA

Contributing Author, Developer of Concept and Materials for Math to Go

Harry Bohan
Professor of Mathematics Education
Sam Houston State University
Huntsville, TX

Program Author, Developer of Philosophy and Grades 3–6

Gerlena Clark
Los Angeles County Mathematics Consultant
Los Angeles, CA

Program Author, Developer of Philosophy and Teacher Training Materials

Heather J. Kelleher
Former Classroom Teacher and Doctoral Student
University of British Columbia
Vancouver, BC, Canada

Program Author, Developer of Philosophy and Grades 1–2

Jean M. Shaw
Professor of Elementary Education
University of Mississippi
University, MS

Contributing Author, Developer of Kindergarten Level

Charles S. Thompson
Professor of Education
University of Louisville
Louisville, KY

Program Author, Developer of Philosophy and Grades 3–6

Lucia Vega-Garcia
Bilingual Education Director
Santa Clara County Office of Education
San Jose, CA

Contributing Author, Developer of Teacher Support for Students Acquiring English

Acknowledgments

Grateful acknowledgment is made for the use of the following material:

Illustrations
Banners created by Catharine Bennett.
Chris Reed 7, 29, 30, 33, 34, 44, 45, 55, 59, 60, 77, 79, 80, 81, 101, 102, 103, 105, 106; **Dave Winter** 16, 19, 20, 21, 25, 26, 40, 47, 48, 65, 67, 68, 73, 74, 89, 90, 91, 92, 94, 95, 97, 99, 100. All other illustrations by **Ligature, Inc.**

Photos
All photographs by **Tony Scarpetta Photography** except for the following: **Allan Landau** Cover, i; **Sharon Hoogstraten** Back Cover; © **PhotoDisc** Work mats; **Tracey Wheeler** iv, 3, 54, 56, 57, 61, 62, 70, 101, 102, 104.

Developed and produced by Ligature

Printed in the U.S.A. ISBN: 0-395-67908-7
123456789-WC-99 98 97 96 95 94

Specialists

Brenda Gentry-Norton
Research Associate
Program for Complex Instruction
Stanford University
Palo Alto, CA

Consultant for Assessment Philosophy and Materials

Brenda Glen
Classroom Teacher
Balderas Elementary School
Fresno, CA

Field Test Coordinator and Developer of Teacher's Edition Notes, Grades 5–6

Joan L. Hopkins
Classroom Teacher
Escondido Elementary School
Palo Alto, CA

Field Test Coordinator and Developer of Teacher's Edition Notes, Grades K–2

Betty Iehl
Educational Consultant
San Gabriel, CA

Developer of Teacher's Edition Notes, Grades 4 and 6

National Center to Improve the Tools of Educators
Douglas Carnine, Director
Edward Kameenui, Associate Director
University of Oregon
Eugene, OR

Developer of Alternate Strategies Materials, Grades 2–6

Mary Anne O'Neal
Educational Consultant
Carson, CA

Developer of Teacher's Edition Notes, Grades 3 and 5

Annie Podesto
Staff Development Specialist
Stockton Unified School District
Stockton, CA

Consultant for Assessment Philosophy and Materials

Sally Y. Wong
Title VII Adviser
Los Angeles Unified School District
Los Angeles, CA

Developer of Teacher's Edition Notes, Grades 3–6

Field Test Teachers

Kindergarten Modules

Traci Assad, Fall River Summer School Program, Fall River, MA • **Susanne Burke,** Holmes School, Dorchester, MA • **Leland Clarke,** Holmes School, Dorchester, MA • **Beverly Letendre,** Fall River Summer School Program, Fall River, MA • **Sarah Outten,** Slade Regional Catholic School, Glen Burnie, MD • **Debbie L. Rea,** Escondido School, Stanford, CA • **Pat Robinson,** Escondido School, Stanford, CA

Grade 1 Modules

Robin Crawley, Holmes School, Dorchester, MA • **Nancy Matthews,** Dudley School, Dudley, MA • **Mary Miller,** Holmes School, Dorchester, MA • **Johanna Roses,** Baker School, Chestnut Hill, MA • **Elaine Kuritani Tsumura,** Marrama School, Denver, CO

Grade 2 Modules

Najwa Abdul-Tawwab, Holmes School, Dorchester, MA • **Mary Jane Brown,** Forwood School, Wilmington, DE • **Joan L. Hopkins,** Escondido School, Stanford, CA • **Dorene Odom,** Holmes School, Dorchester, MA • **Ida Wellington,** Washington School, Oakland, CA

Grade 3 Modules

Robin Burstein, Greenwood School, Des Moines, IA • **Joanne Castellano,** Slade Regional Catholic School, Glen Burnie, MD • **Diane Rezek Fator,** Emerson School, Berwyn, IL • **Linda Griffiths,** Kennedy School, San Diego, CA • **Michele Hilbing,** Slade Regional Catholic School, Glen Burnie, MD • **Sharnell Jackson,** Decatur School, Chicago, IL • **Janet M. Laws,** Lombardy School, Wilmington, DE • **Patricia Y. Lynch,** Lombardy School, Wilmington, DE • **Efraín Meléndez,** Dacotah School, Los Angeles, CA • **Doris Miles,** Sandburg School, Wheaton, IL • **Ricki Raymond,** Piper School, Berwyn, IL • **Bonnie Schindler,** Kennedy School, San Diego, CA • **Theresa Sievers,** Komensky School, Berwyn, IL • **Kimberly Bassett Whitehead,** Lombardy School, Wilmington, DE

Grade 4 Modules

Lynda Alexander, St. Elizabeth School, Chicago, IL • **Betty Coleman,** Parkman School, Chicago, IL • **Karen DeRon-Head,** Armour School, Chicago, IL • **Keith Libert,** Escondido School, Stanford, CA • **Joe Montoya,** Mann School, Rapid City, SD • **Robert Poncé,** Niños Heroes School, Chicago, IL

Grade 5 Modules

Lynnise H. Akinkunle-Gool, Niños Heroes School, Chicago, IL • **Doris Buffo,** Balderas School, Fresno, CA • **Ronni K. Cohen,** Burnett School, Wilmington, DE • **Valerie De George,** Greeley School, Chicago, IL • **Brenda Glen,** Balderas School, Fresno, CA • **Cynthia L. Lew,** Madison School, Pomona, CA • **Lisa Palacios,** Pleasant Hill School, Carol Stream, IL • **Kathryn Peecher,** Revere School, Chicago, IL • **Cindy Sardo,** Burnett School, Wilmington, DE • **Henry A. Simmons,** Balderas School, Fresno, CA • **Delorise Singley,** Oakwood Windsor School, Aiken, SC • **Cecilia Maria Vasquez,** Balderas School, Fresno, CA • **Michelle Wilson,** Jefferson School, Fresno, CA

Grade 6 Modules

Dorothy Cooper Jones, Banneker Achievement Center, Gary, IN • **Albert Martinez,** Marianna Avenue School, Los Angeles, CA • **Sharon Oechsel,** Hiawatha School, Berwyn, IL • **Christopher G. Reising,** Kennedy School, San Diego, CA • **Lee Wirth,** Pershing School, Berwyn, IL

Reviewers

Kathryn A. Alexander, Macon Middle School, Brunswick, GA (Grade 6 modules) • **Sherry Bailey,** Richland School District #2, Columbia, SC (Grade 5 modules) • **Elsbeth G. Bellemere,** Scarborough School District, Scarborough, ME (Grade 5 modules) • **Sharon L. Cannon,** Myrtle Beach Middle School, Myrtle Beach, SC (Grade 6 modules) • **Cleo Charging,** White Shield School, Roseglen, ND (Grade K modules) • **Judy C. Curtis,** Colfax School, Denver, CO (Grade 3 modules) • **Myra S. Dietz,** Carroll School, Rochester, NY (Grade 6 modules) • **W. L. Duncker,** Midland School District, Midland, TX (Grade 5 modules) • **Donna Marie Falat,** Longfellow School, Bridgeport, CT (Grade 2 modules) • **Linda Gojak,** Hawken School, Lendhurst, OH (Grade 6 modules) • **Annette D. Ham,** Waltersville School, Bridgeport, CT (Grade 5 modules) • **Feliciano Mendoza,** Miles Avenue School, Huntington Park, CA (Grades 5 and 6 modules) • **Kenneth Millett,** Department of Mathematics, University of California, Santa Barbara, CA (Grade 6 modules) • **Rita Nappi,** Read School, Bridgeport, CT (Grade 4 modules) • **Mahesh Sharma,** Cambridge College, Cambridge, MA (Grades K and 6 modules) • **Patricia E. Smith,** Crosswell School, Easley, SC (Grades 3 and 4 modules) • **Bonnie Townzen,** Lubin School, Sacramento, CA (Grade 1 modules) • **Angelia W. Whiting,** Beardsley School, Bridgeport, CT (Grade 1 modules) • **Pamela Yoka,** Covedale School, Cincinnati, OH (Grade K modules)

Math Power

This year you will build **math power**. Math power means being able to use math whenever you need it. You will be able to do math at school, at home, or anywhere. You can use math every day to solve all kinds of problems.

Drawing to Learn

You will draw pictures to find answers to questions.

Using Math Tools

You will learn how and when to use counters, calculators, and computers.

Solving Problems

You will figure out how to solve problems.

Talking About It

You will talk with others about the math you do.

Name ____________________

Sorting Toys

1 Write the sorting rules.

Rule: ____________________

Rule: ____________________

2 Where do these toys go?

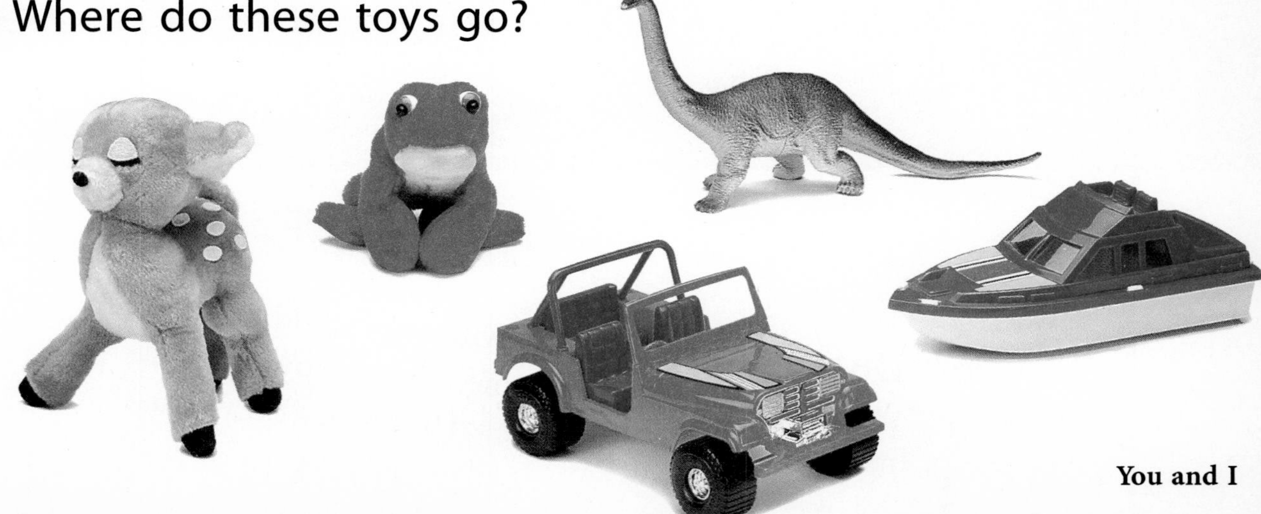

3 Sort the toys.
Use the cutouts on the next page.

Dear Family: Discuss with your child the different things that you sort at home, such as toys, dishes, mail, and groceries. What sorting rules do you use?

Use these cutouts with page **2**.

Name ____________________

Sorting Different Ways

1. Choose a rule to sort the pattern blocks. Draw the shapes.

Group A	Group B

2. Write how many.

Group A ____

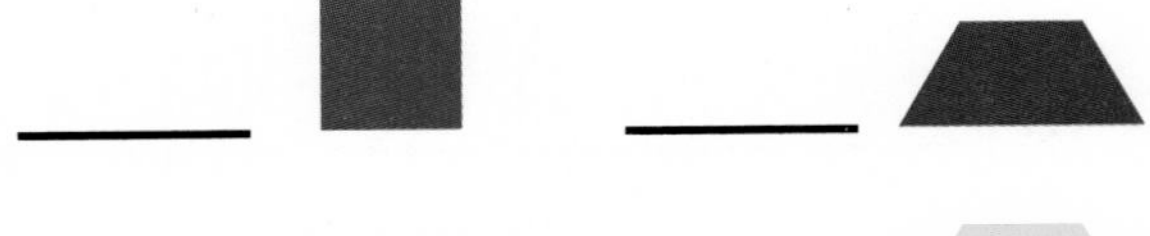

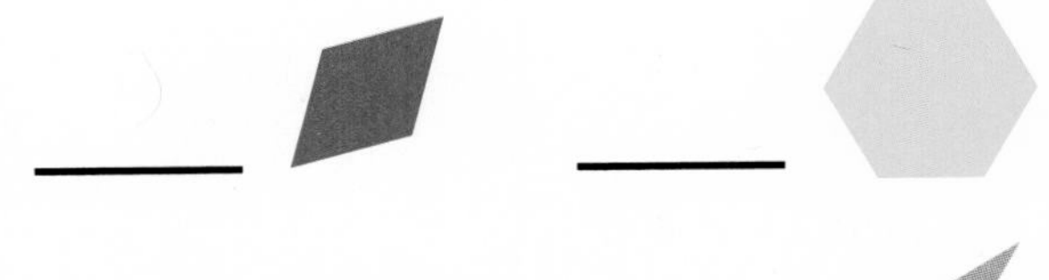

3. Write how many.

Group B ____

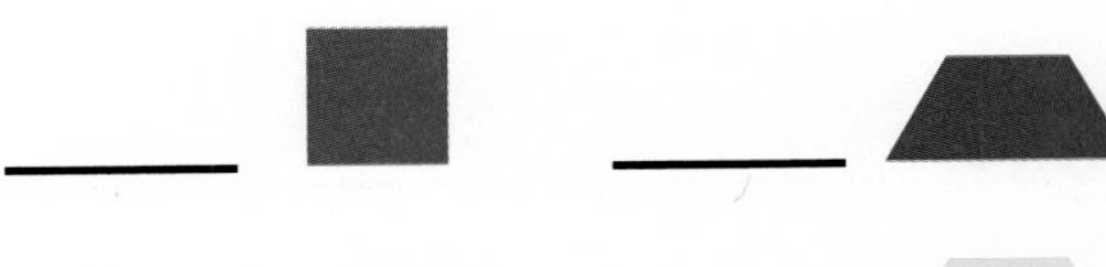

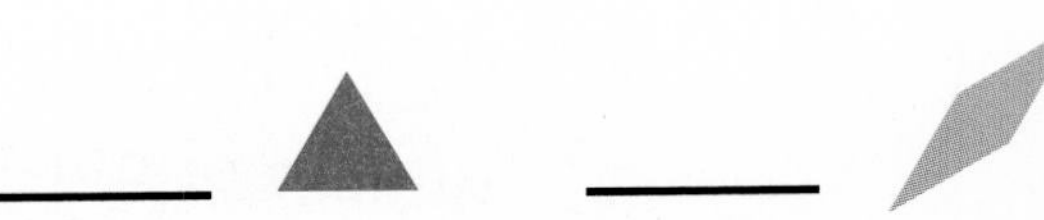

Write the sorting rule for each picture.

4

Rule: ______________ Rule: ______________

5

Rule: ______________ Rule: ______________

6

Rule: ______________ Rule: ______________

Dear Family: Invite your child to help you sort laundry or other objects at home. Explain your reasoning as you sort.

Name ______________________

Counting and Comparing

Count and write how many.

1 ______ (sailboat)

2 ______ (kite)

3 ______ (pail)

4 ______ (beach ball)

5 ______ (umbrella)

6 ______ (book)

Compare each drawing below to the big picture.

7 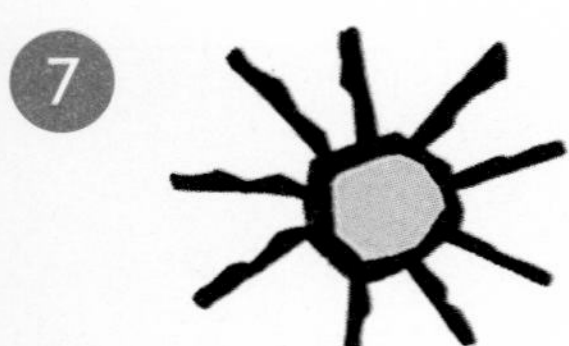

There are _____ more rays.

8 

There are _____ fewer spots.

9 

There are _____ fewer windows.

10 

There are _____ more petals.

11 

There are _____ fewer wheels.

12 

There are _____ more branches.

Dear Family: Take a walk through your neighborhood or home, comparing similar objects and using *more than* or *less than*.

Name ____________________

Counting Cubes

Write the number of cubes.

____ 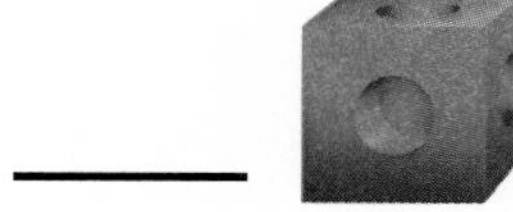 ____  ____ cubes in all

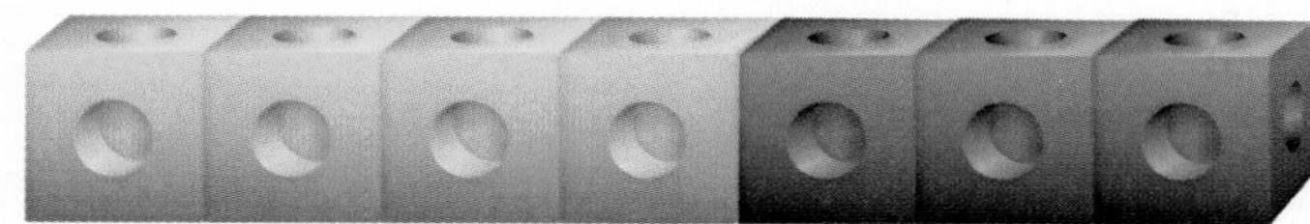

____  ____ 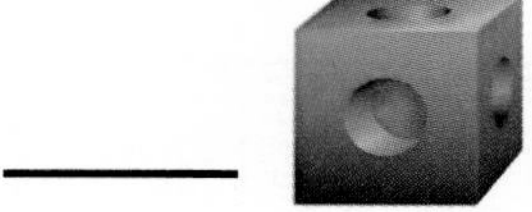 ____ cubes in all

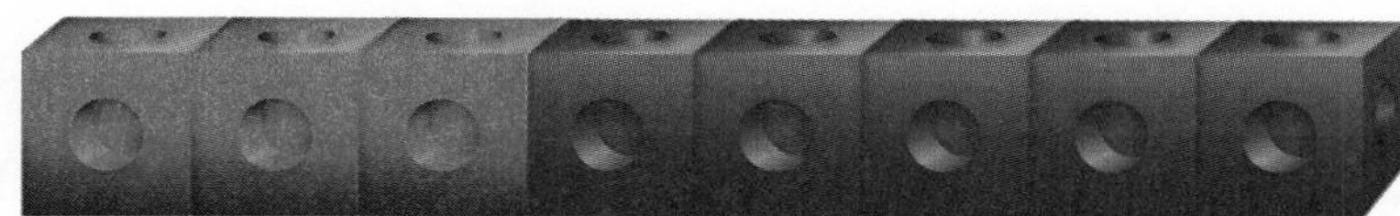

____ 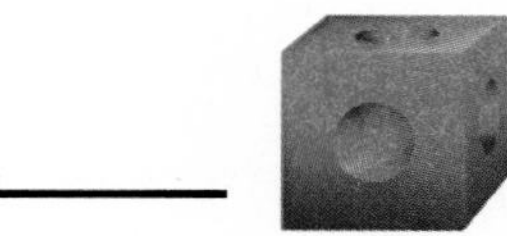 ____ 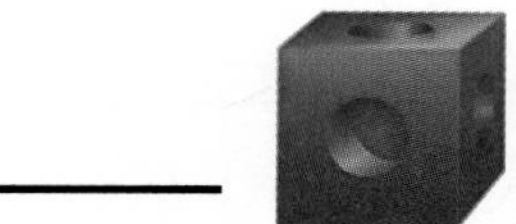 ____ cubes in all

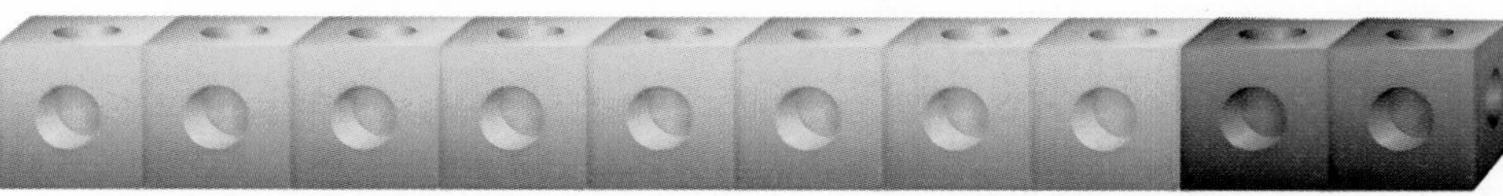

____ 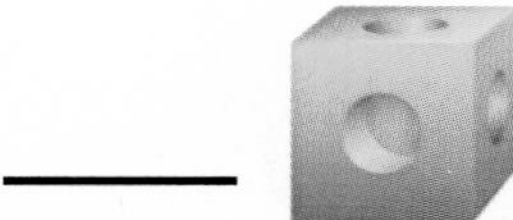 ____ 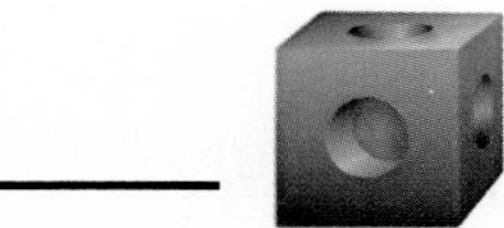 ____ cubes in all

Use two colors to color the cube trains.
Write the number of cubes.

5 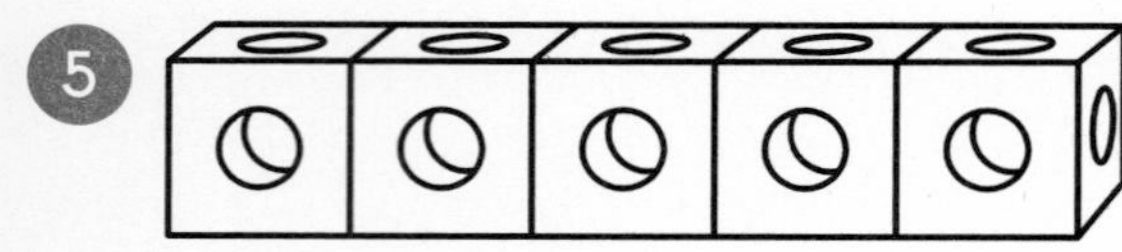

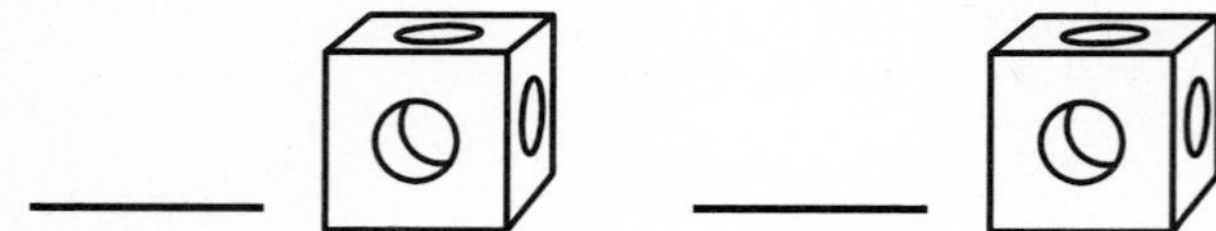

____ ____ ____ cubes in all

6 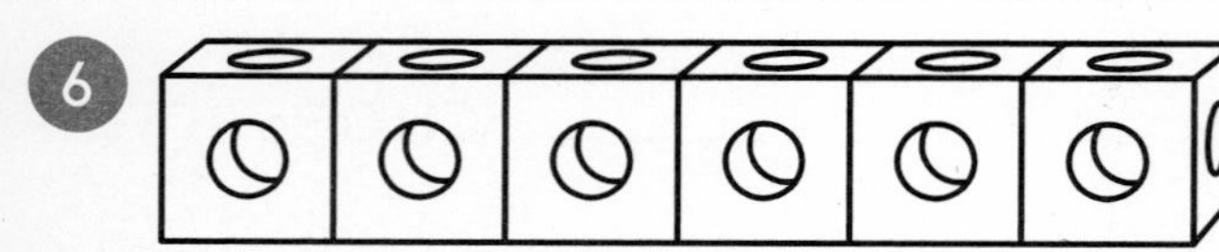

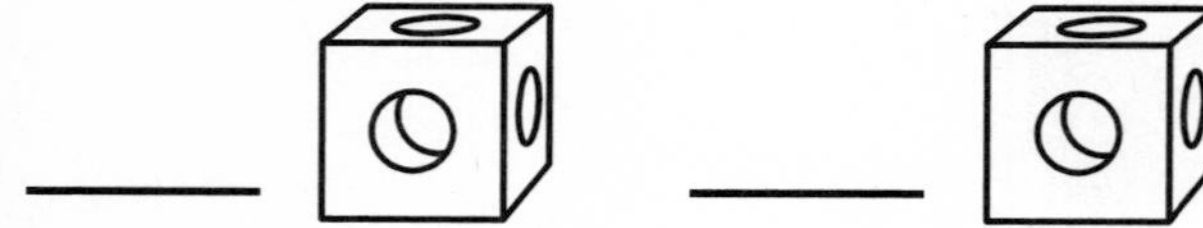

____ ____ ____ cubes in all

7 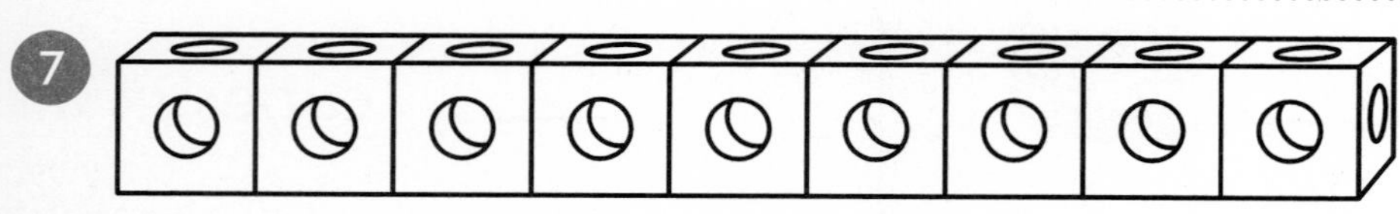

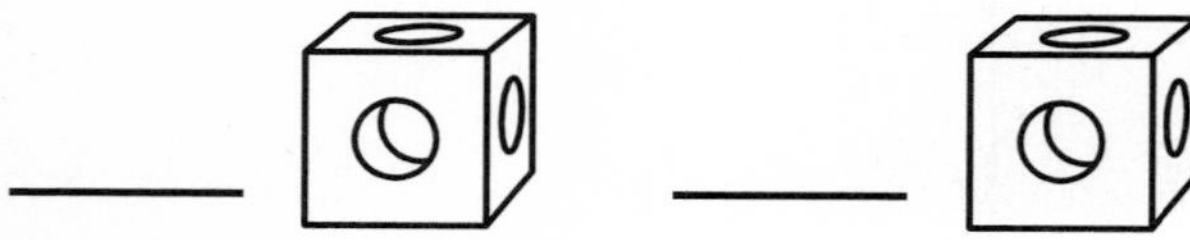

____ ____ ____ cubes in all

8 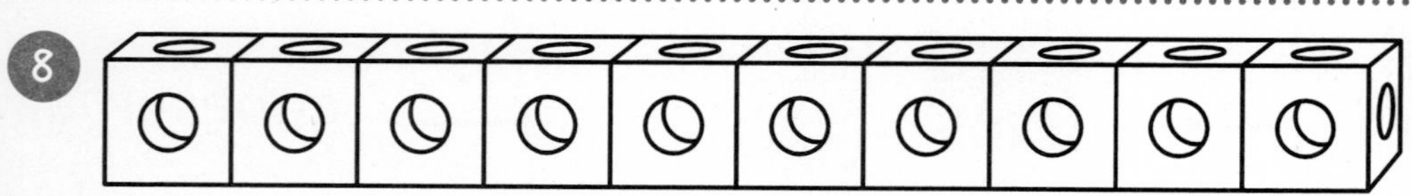

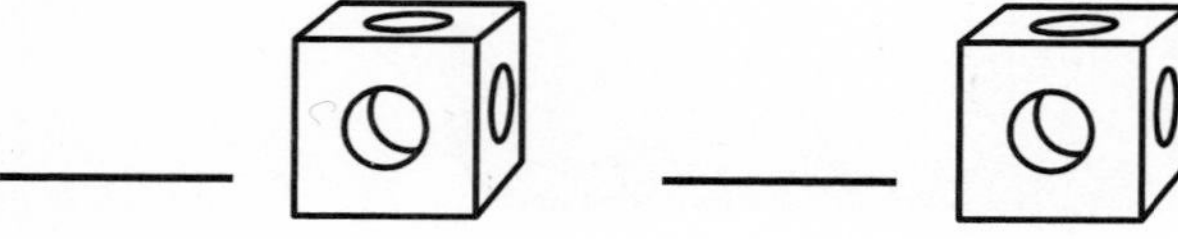

____ ____ ____ cubes in all

Dear Family: With your child, look for things at home that are divided into parts, such as pizza, puzzles, and pies.

Name ________________________________

Counting Candles

1 Listen to the stories.
Show the ages with candles.

Draw the candles on the cake.
Write the sum.

2 4

I am ______ years old.

3

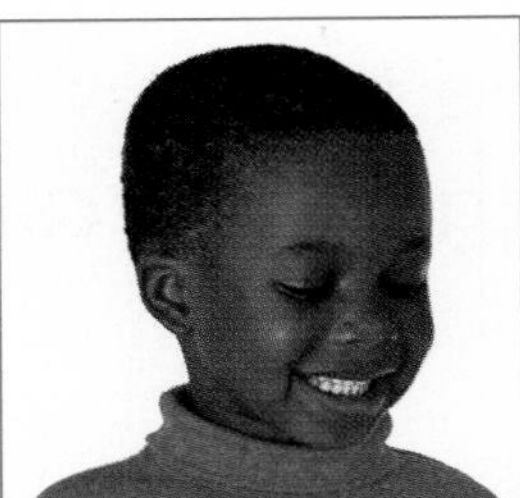

4 3

I am ______ years old.

4

5 2

I am ______ years old.

5

6 0

I am ______ years old.

Dear Family: Discuss with your child things that change as he or she gets older, such as bedtime, allowance, chores, and grade level.

Name____________________________________

What's the Date?

1 Write the dates of this week.

Sunday	Monday	Tuesday	Wednesday	Thursday	Friday	Saturday

2 Write the name of the day.
Draw a picture about each day.

Yesterday was ________________.

Today is ________________.

Tomorrow will be ________________.

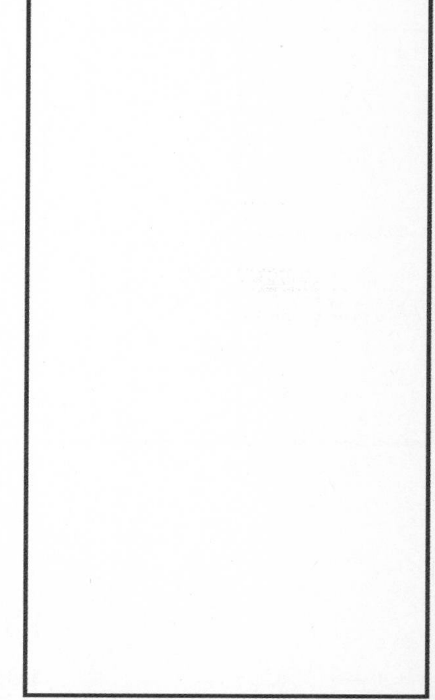

3 Listen. Fill in the calendar.
Add your own pictures.

____

Sunday	Monday	Tuesday	Wednesday	Thursday	Friday	Saturday

Dear Family: Discuss with your child things that your family does at different times of the year, such as going on picnics or trips, or celebrating holidays.

Name ______________________________

Symmetry Pictures

Follow these steps.

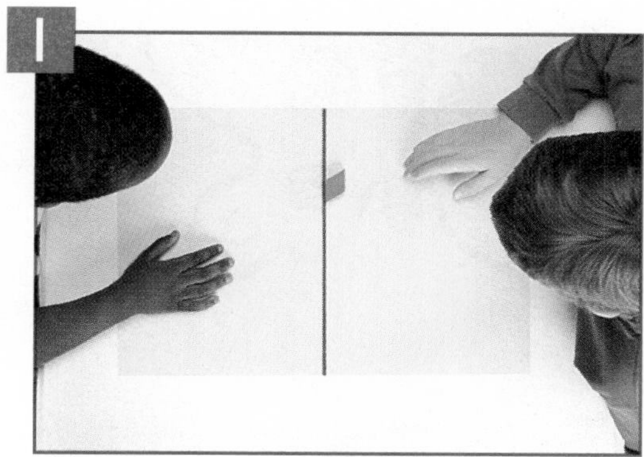

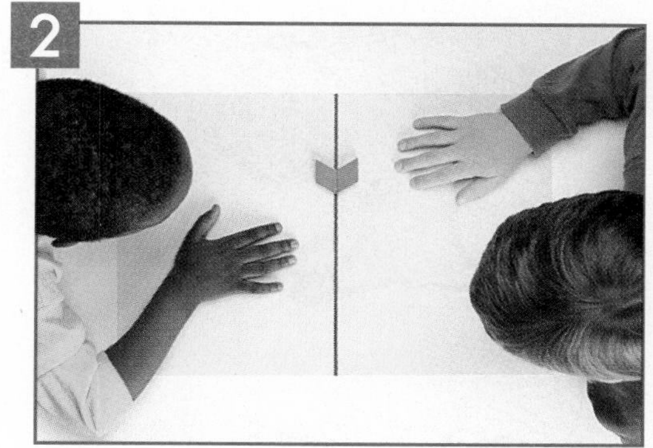

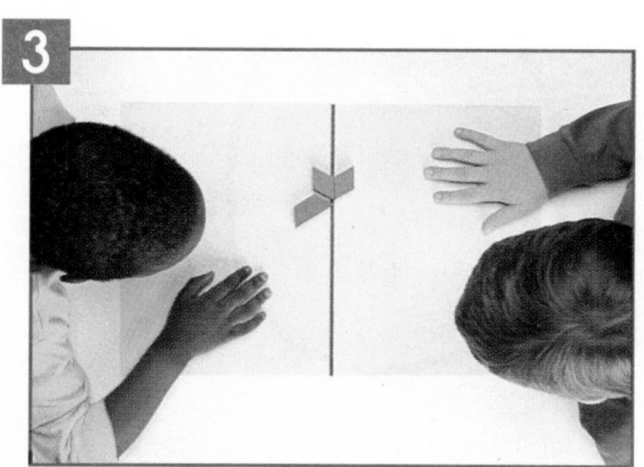

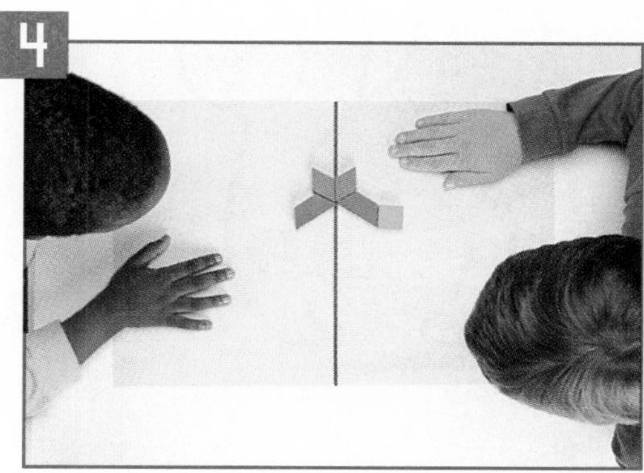

1 Use words or pictures to tell about your design.

Ring the shapes with symmetry.
Draw the lines of symmetry.

2

3
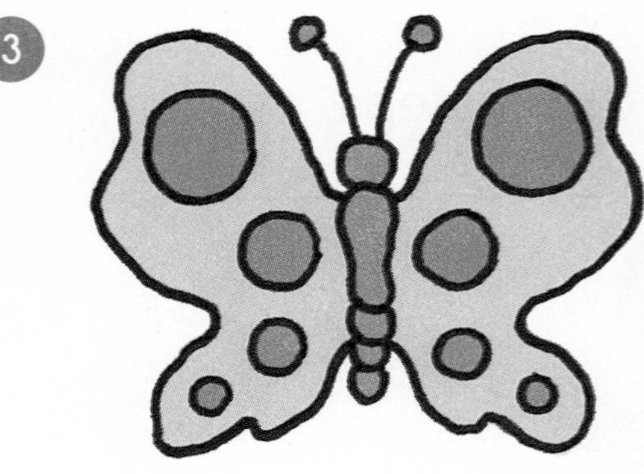

4

5

6
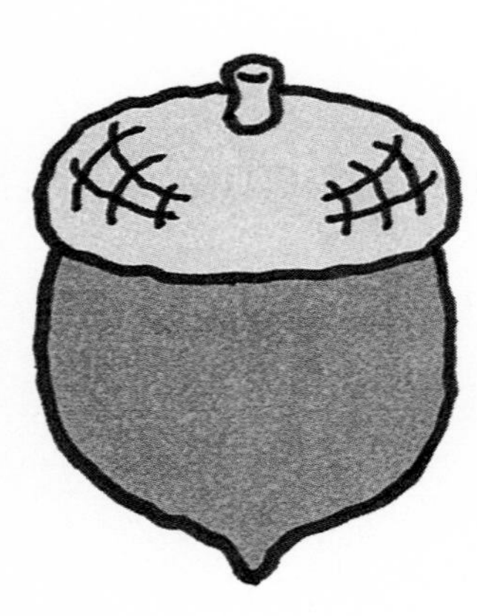

7

Dear Family: With your child, look for symmetrical things around your home and neighborhood. Draw the symmetrical things you find.

Name ______________________________

Look at the Parts

Draw the other half to show symmetry.

1

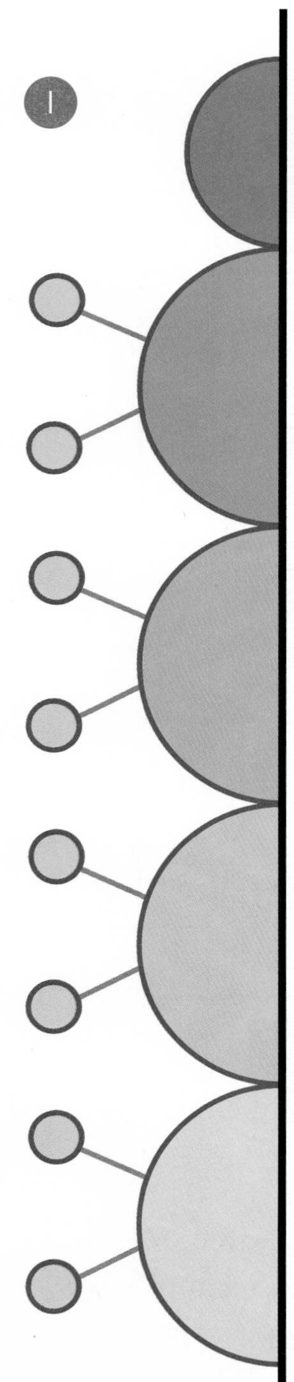

2

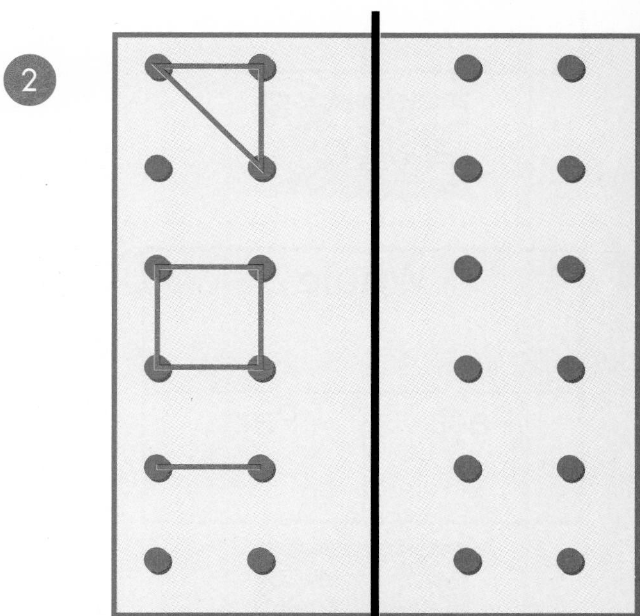

3

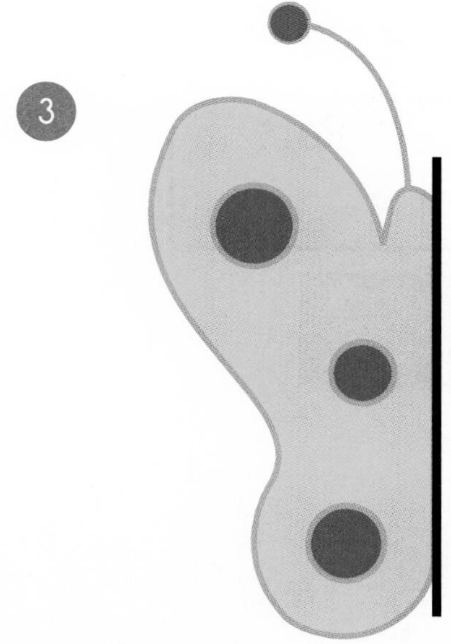

Write the whole and the parts.

4

Whole	
Part	Part

5

Whole	
Part	Part

6

Whole	
Part	Part

7

Whole	
Part	Part

8

Whole	
Part	Part

9

Whole	
Part	Part

Dear Family: Together, look for things at home or in your neighborhood that come in doubles. For example, shoes, tires, and eggs come in doubles. Look for others!

Name ________________________________

Pattern Puzzles

Ring the pattern stem.

1

2

3

1 2 3 4 1 2 3 4 1 2 3 4

4

5

6

Continue the pattern.

7

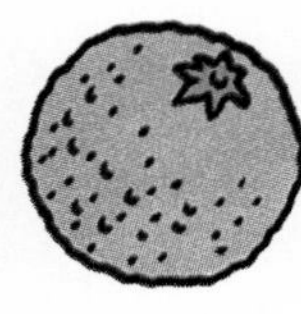

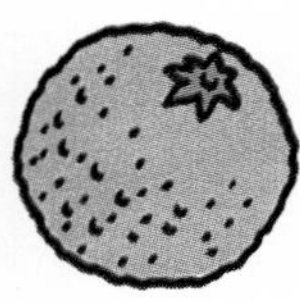

8

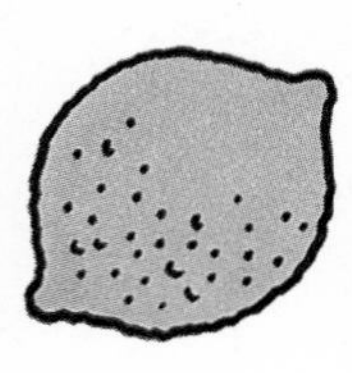

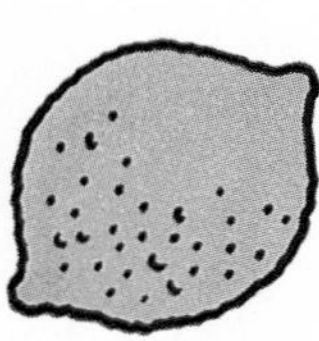

9

B B A B B A B B ___ ___ ___ ___

10

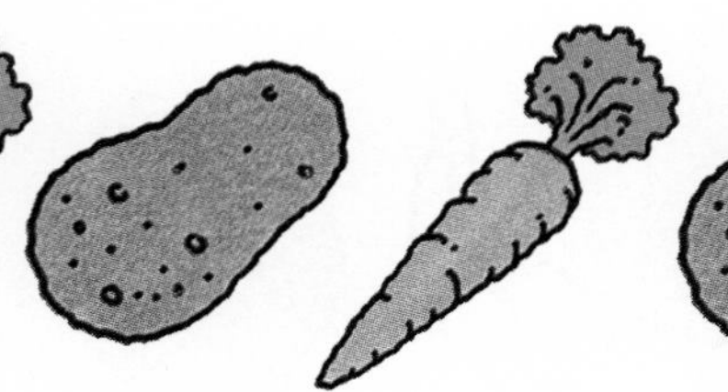

11

1 2 3 1 2 3 1 2 ___ ___ ___

Dear Family: Together with your child, make patterns using common household items, such as eating utensils or toys.

Name ________________________________

What's Missing?

Fill in the missing part.

1

3 3 4 3 3 4 3 3 4 ______

2

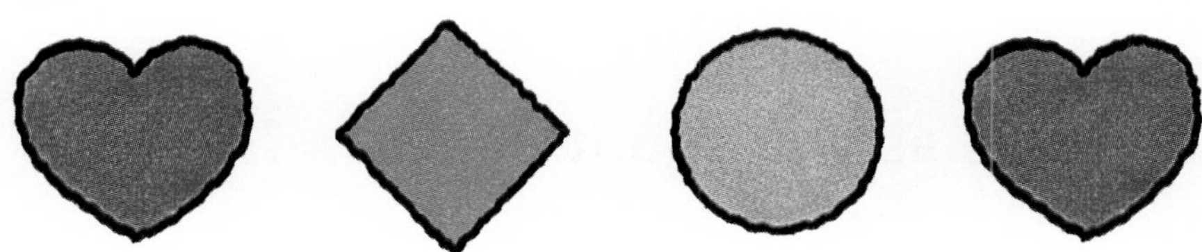

3

4

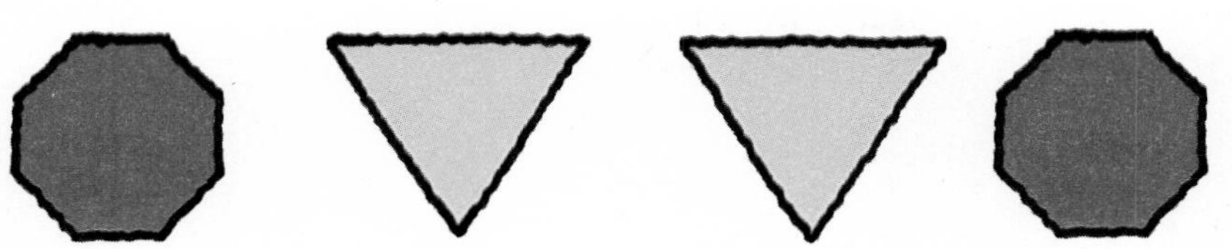

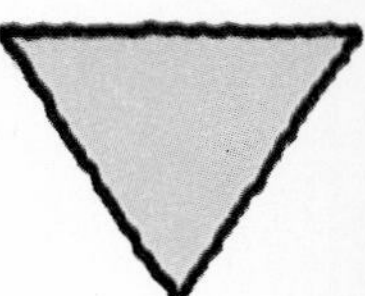

5. Start at **2**. Connect the dots as you count by **2**s.

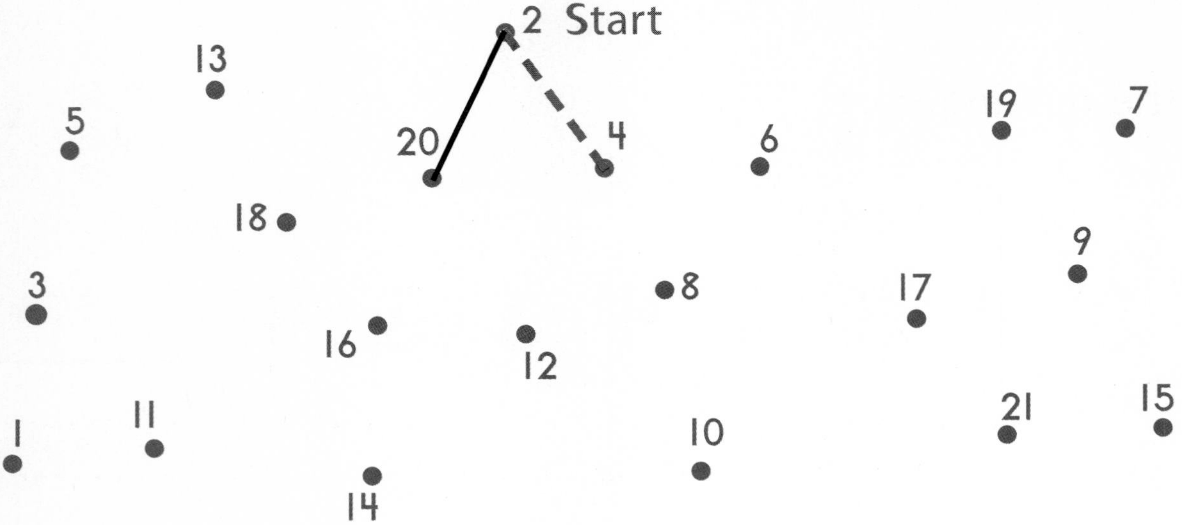

6. Start at **3**. Connect the dots as you count by **3**s.

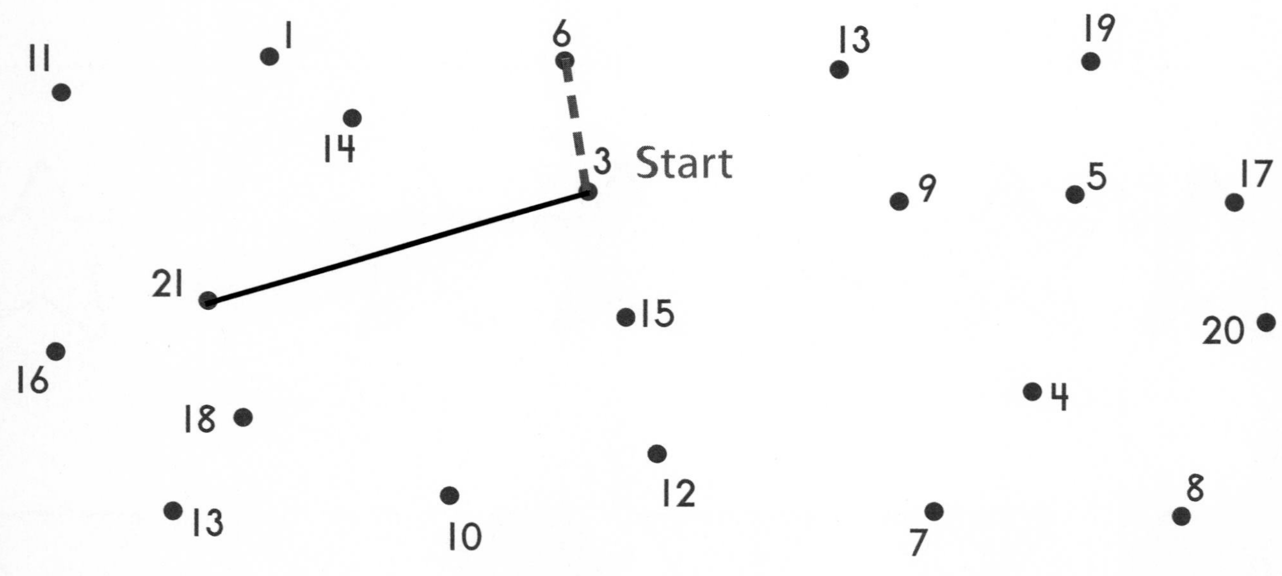

Dear Family: Work with your child to count objects at home by 2s and 3s.

Name ____________________

Coin Counts

Drop 10 pennies.
Write the number of heads and tails.

1  heads ____  tails ____

2  heads ____  tails ____

3  heads ____  tails ____

4  heads ____  tails ____

5  heads ____  tails ____

6  heads ____  tails ____

Tally and total the coins.
Cross out each coin as you tally it.

Coin	Tally	Total
7		
8		
9		

Dear Family: With your child, examine coins in your wallet or pocket. Encourage your child to count the number of each type of coin.

Name ____________________

Take a Look at Ten

Draw shells to make 10.
Write the number.

1 

4 and ____

2 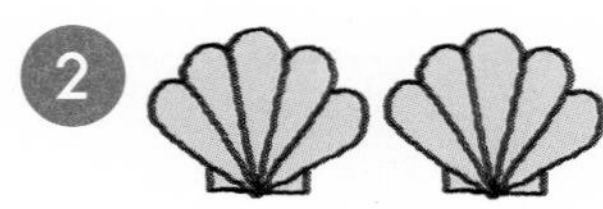

2 and ____

3 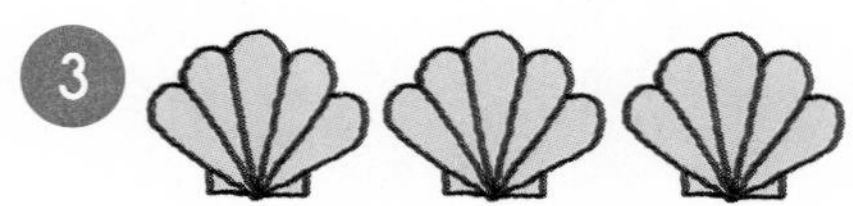

3 and ____

4 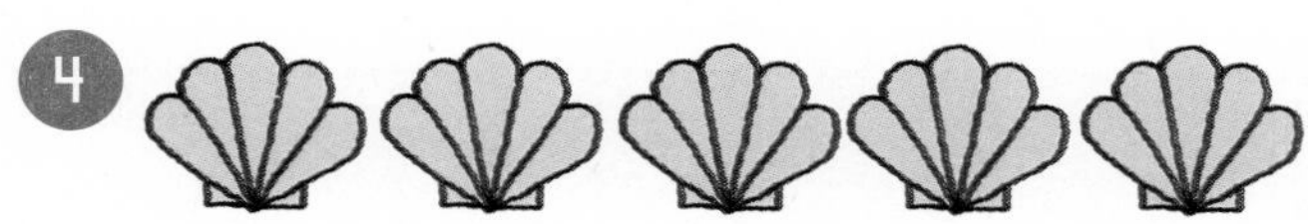

5 and ____

5 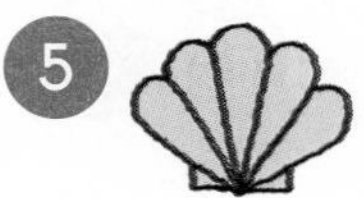

1 and ____

0 and ____

Ring a group of 10.
Then complete the sentence.

12 is 10 and _____ more.

8

13 is 10 and _____ more.

9

19 is 10 and _____ more.

Dear Family: Together with your child, practice identifying each of the numbers from 11 to 20 as "10 and _____ more."

Name ________________________________

Cube Order

1

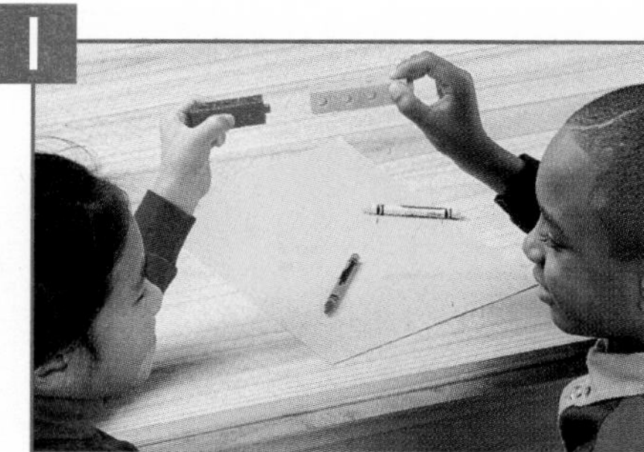

Work with a partner. Make a train of two colors.

2

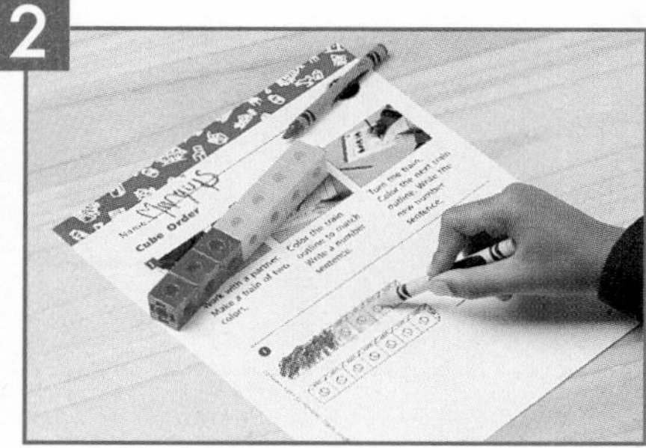

Color the train outline to match. Write a number sentence.

3

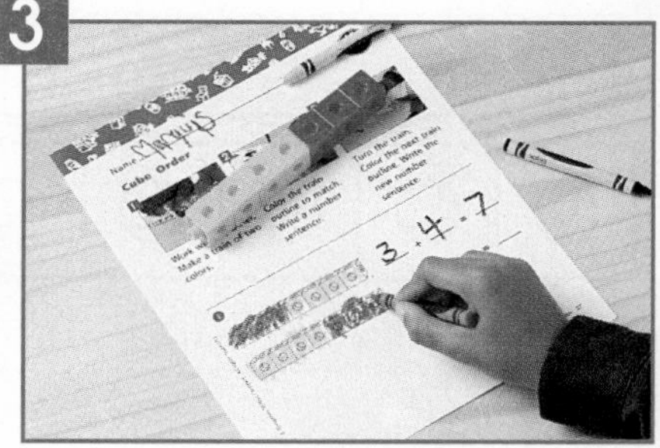

Turn the train. Color the next train outline. Write the new number sentence.

1 7 cubes

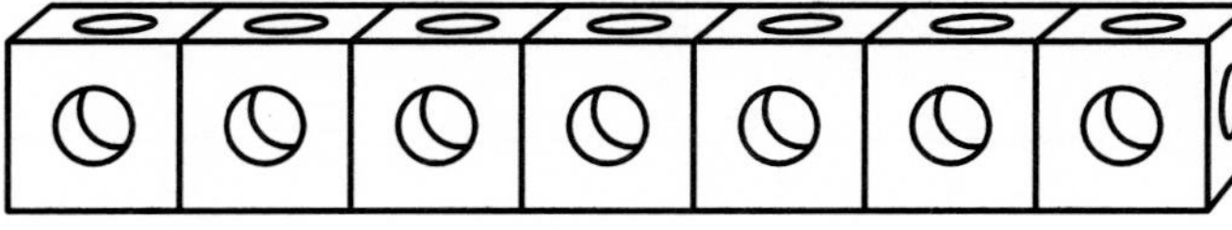

____ + ____ = ____

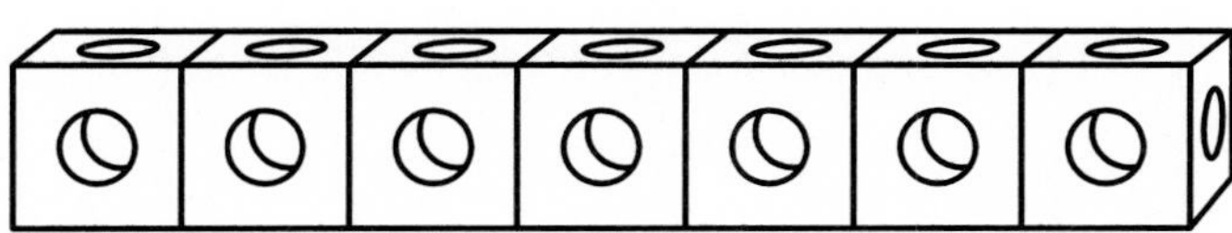

____ + ____ = ____

2 5 cubes

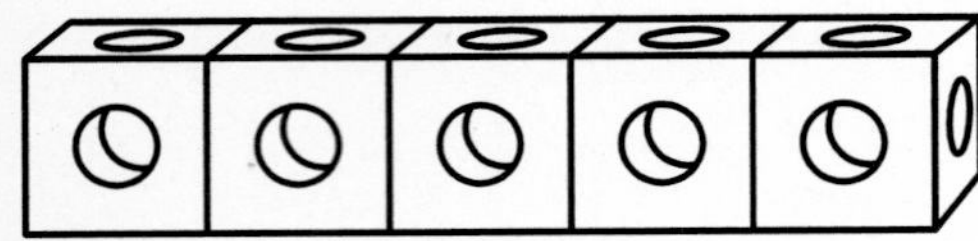

___ + ___ = ___

___ + ___ = ___

3 7 cubes

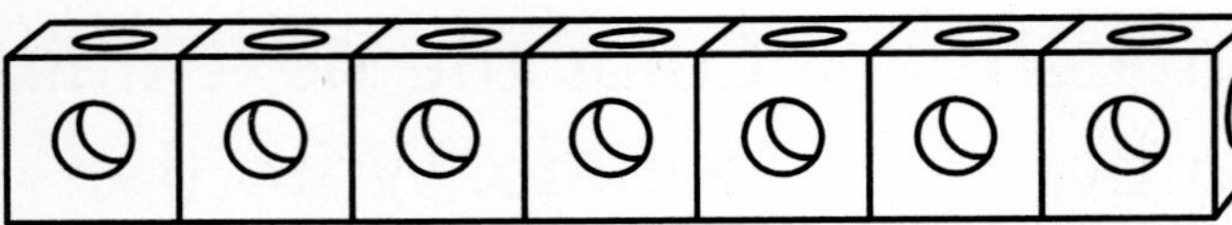

___ + ___ = ___

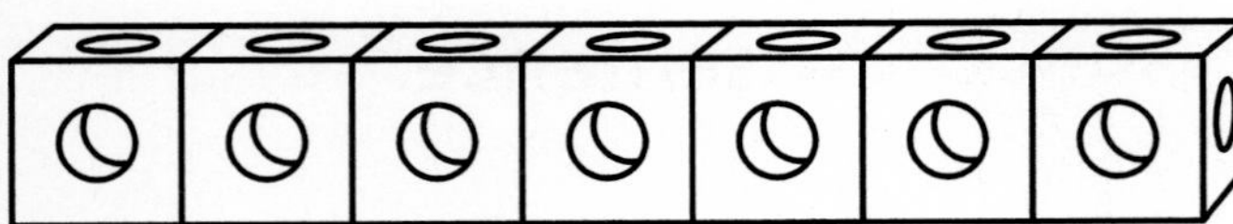

___ + ___ = ___

4 6 cubes

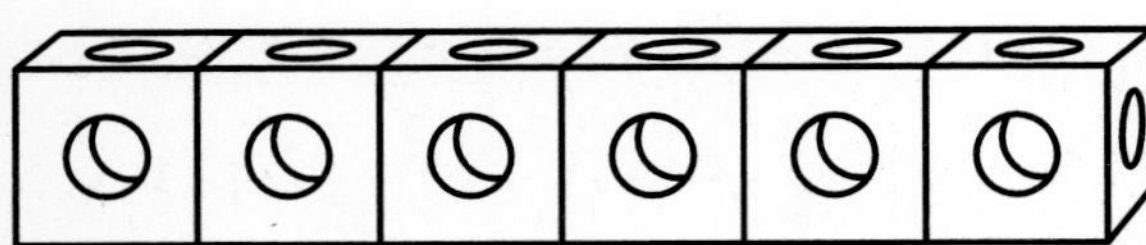

___ + ___ = ___

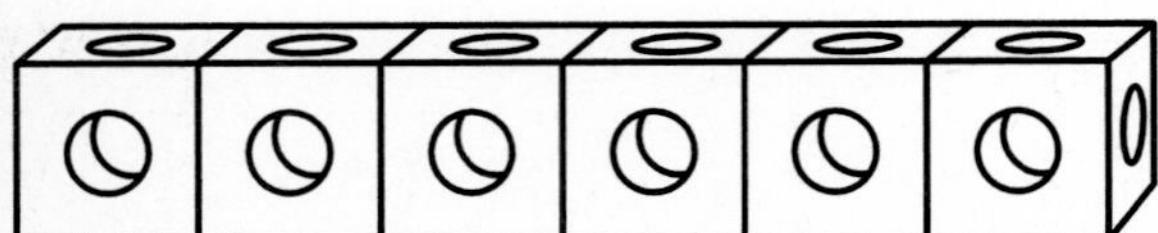

___ + ___ = ___

Dear Family: With your child think of activities in which steps can be done in different sequences (putting clothes in the washer, putting on socks).

Name ______________________________

What Is in the House?

Count how many of each item is in each room.
Write a number sentence to describe the sets.

1 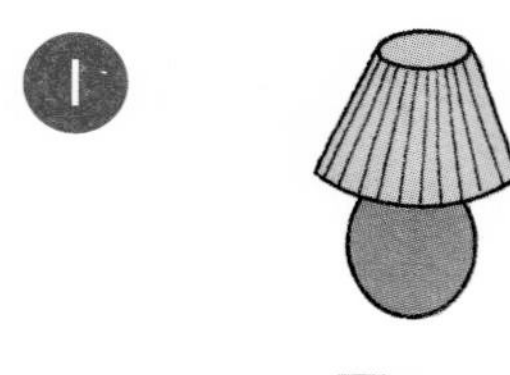 1 + 3 = 4

2  ___ + ___ = ___

3  ___ + ___ = ___

4 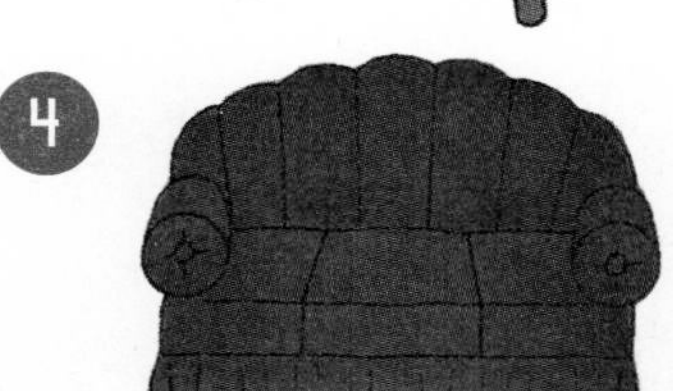 ___ + ___ = ___

5 Draw chairs and tables in each room.

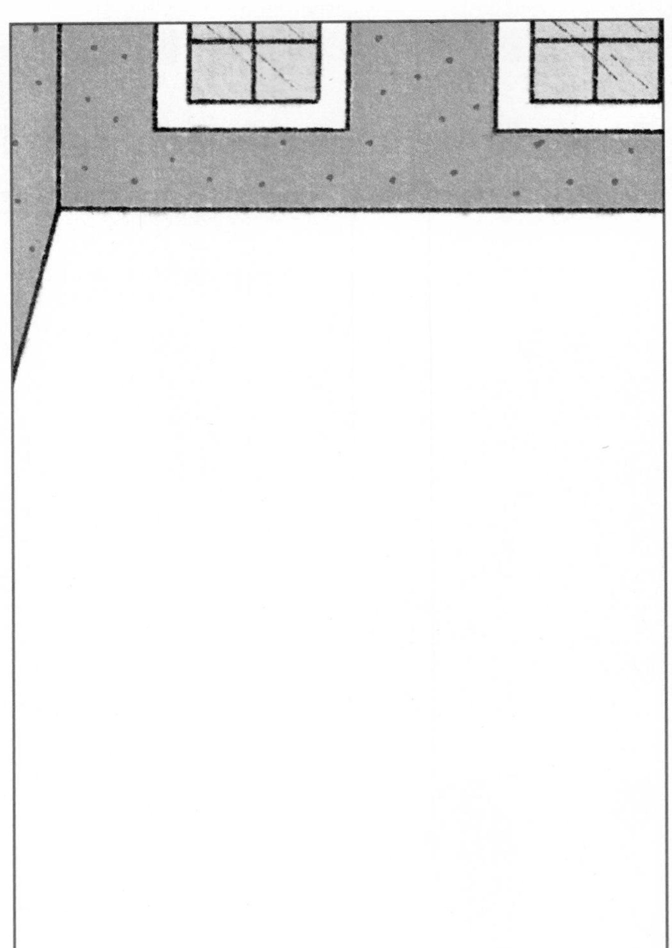

6 Use your drawing to write a number sentence.

___ + ___ = ___

___ + ___ = ___

Dear Family: With your child discuss how many chairs you will need if you invite another family you know to dinner.

Name ____________________

Exploring Length

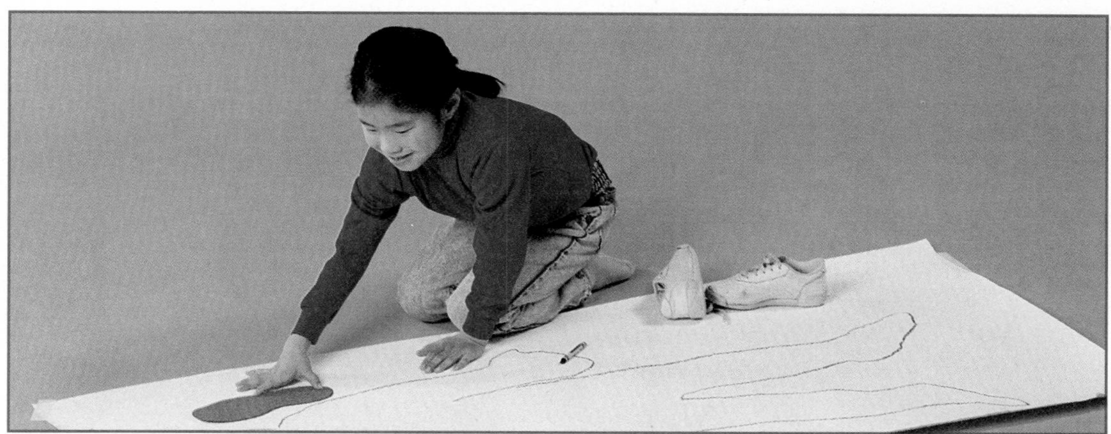

Use your shoe print to measure large objects.

	Object	Shoe Print
1	chalkboard	______
2	______	______
3	______	______
4	______	______
5	______	______

Name two objects about as long as your shoe.

6 ______ 7 ______

Name two objects about as long as a paper clip.

8 ______ 9 ______

Measure the picture.

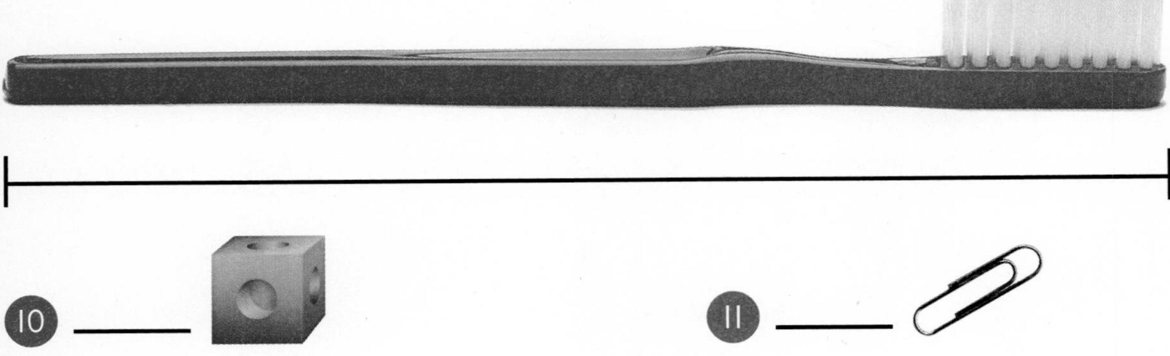

10 ____ cube

11 ____ paper clip

Find these objects.
Measure them with cubes and paper clips.

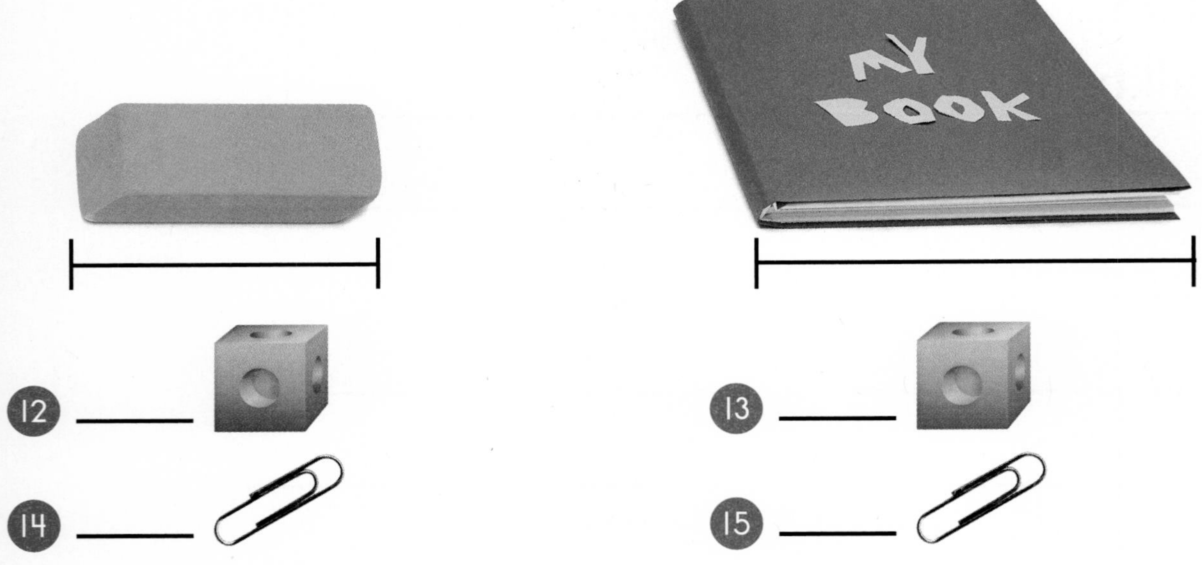

12 ____ cube

13 ____ cube

14 ____ paper clip

15 ____ paper clip

Dear Family: Try using the shoe print or another object to measure things around your home.

Name________________________________

My Measurements

Use cubes to measure the length shown.

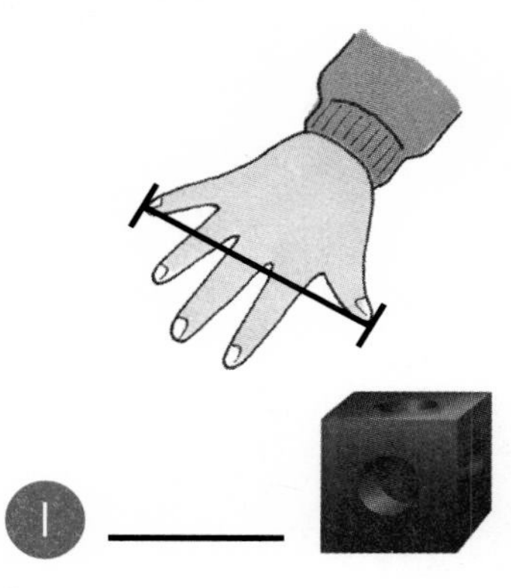

1 ____

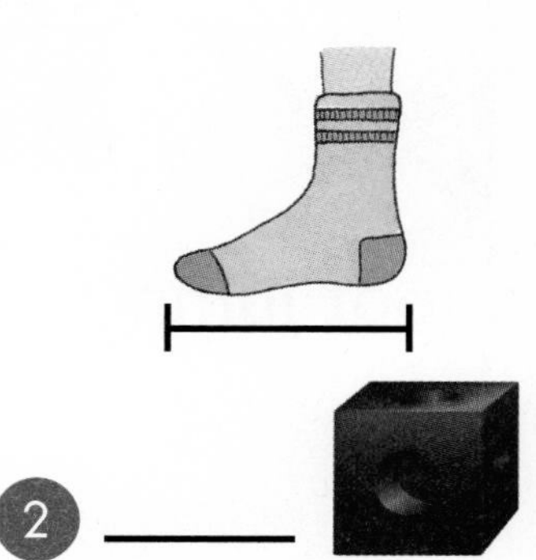

2 ____

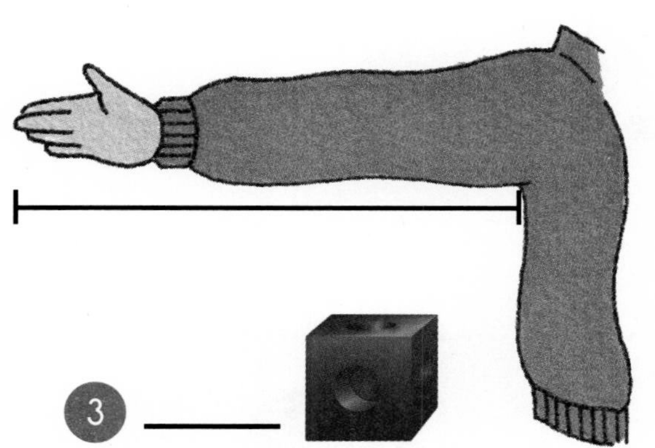

3 ____

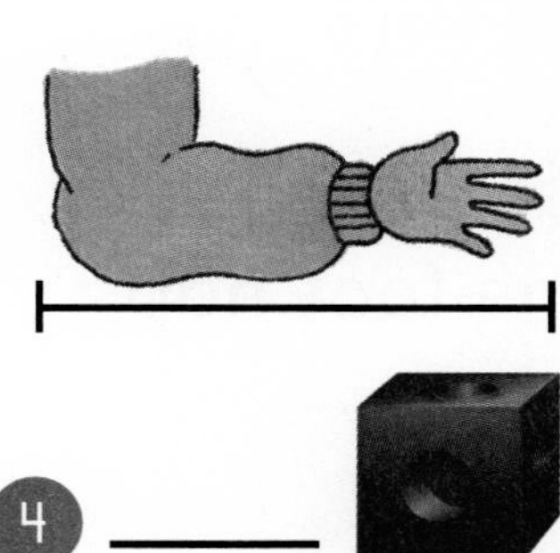

4 ____

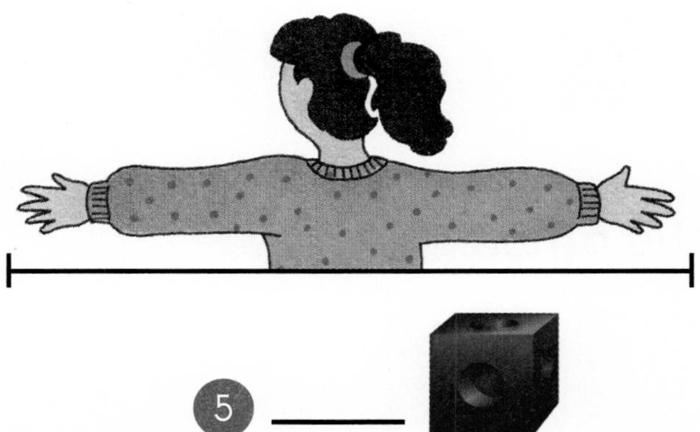

5 ____

Use cubes to measure each distance.

6

two-foot jump

____ 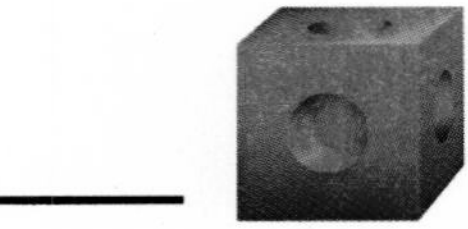

7

same-foot hop

____ 

8

one foot to the other

____ 

Dear Family: You might want to repeat this activity at home. With your child decide which of the methods illustrated above is the best way to go a long distance.

Name____

What Am I?

Ring the block that matches the words.

1. green and big

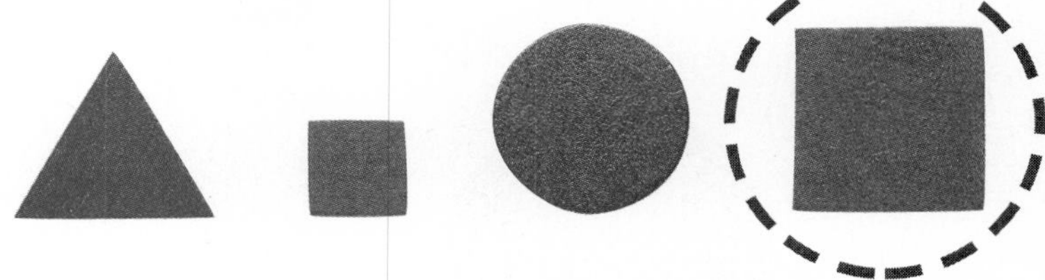

2. blue and big

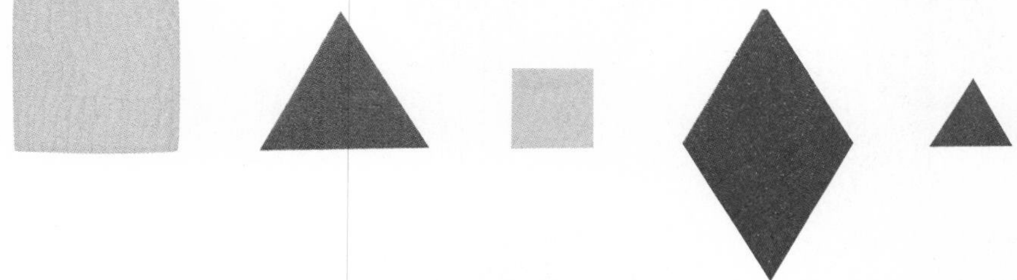

3. round and blue

4. small and a triangle

5. big, not square, and yellow

6 Listen to the clues.

Dear Family: With your child sort ten objects into two groups. Write corresponding number sentences, such as 4+ 6= 10 and 6+ 4= 10.

Name ____________________

What Are the Blocks?

Label the groups.

1

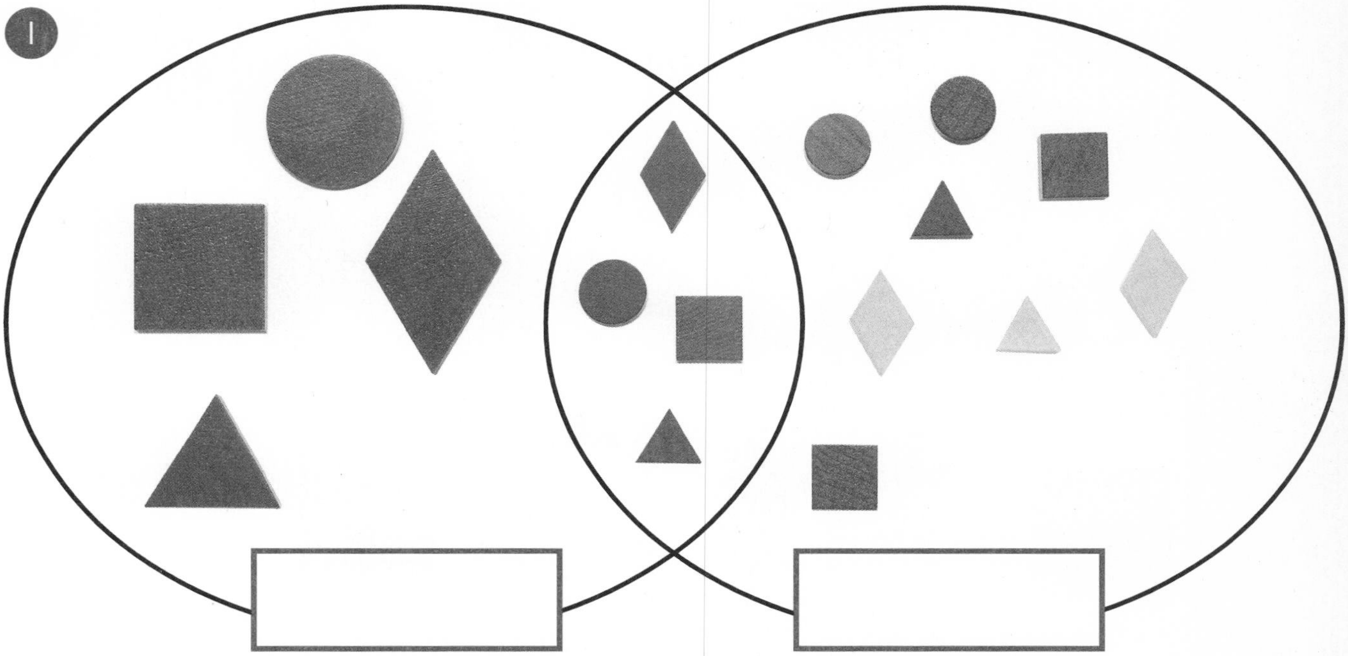

2

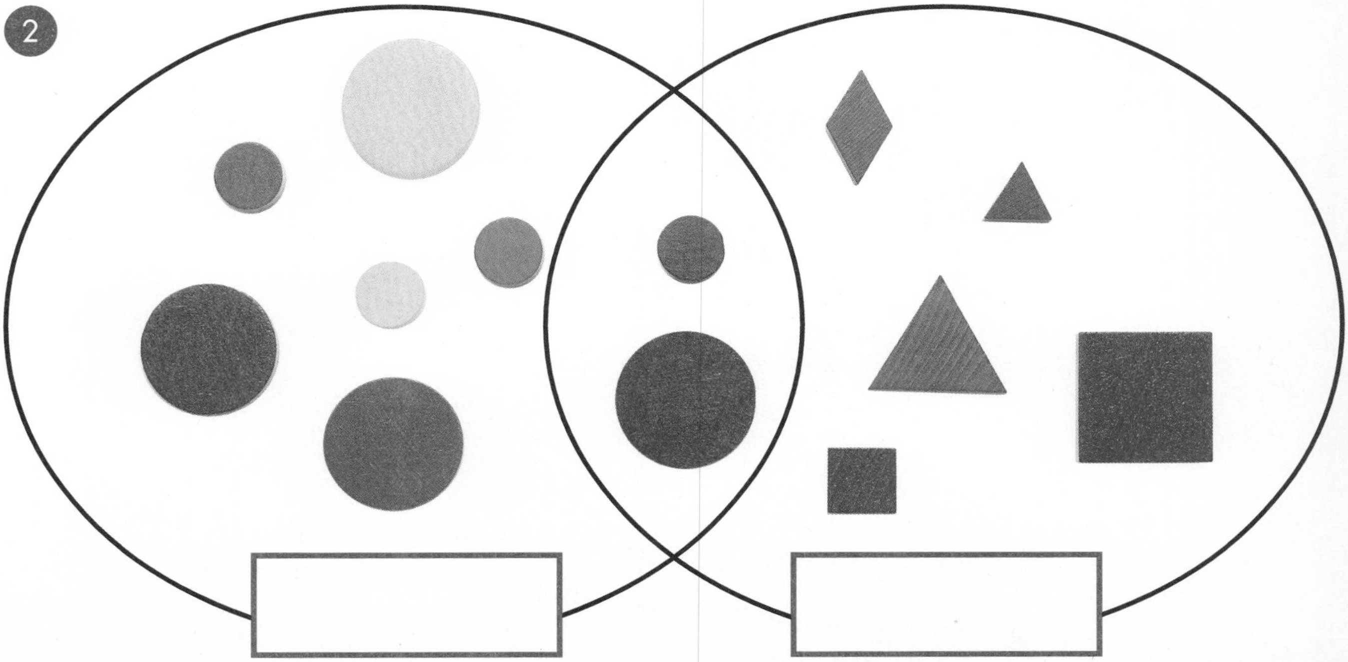

Ring the right block.

3 It is large.
It has more than **3** sides.
It is not green.

4 It is not a circle.
It is not yellow.
It is not a triangle.

Dear Family: Play a logic game like I Spy together. Give one clue at a time until a player identifies the object in the room.

Name ______________________________

What Can Shapes Do?

Decide your stacking rule.
Record your findings.

Object	Never	Sometimes	Always
1			
2			
3			
4			
5			
6			

Draw a picture to solve each problem.

7

8

9

10 Draw your own problem picture.

Correct your picture.

Dear Family: Encourage your child to point out and describe any geometric solids he or she sees while doing household chores such as putting away groceries.

Name________________________________

How Many of Each?

Record your findings.

Object	Faces	Points/Corners	Edges
1 			
2			
3 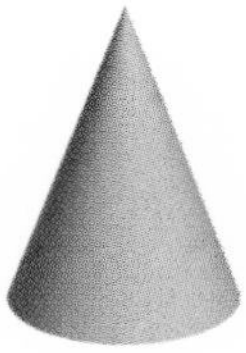			
4 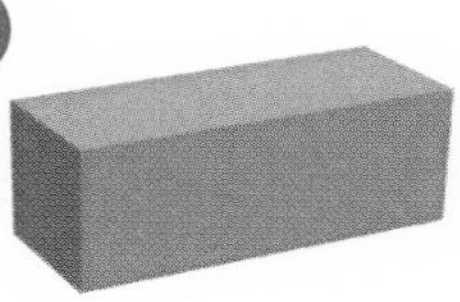			
5 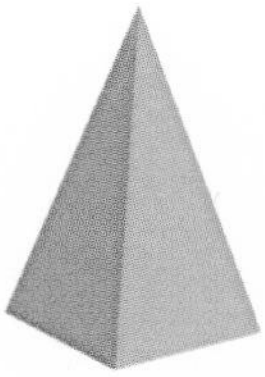			
6 			

7 Draw lines to connect each object to a shape.

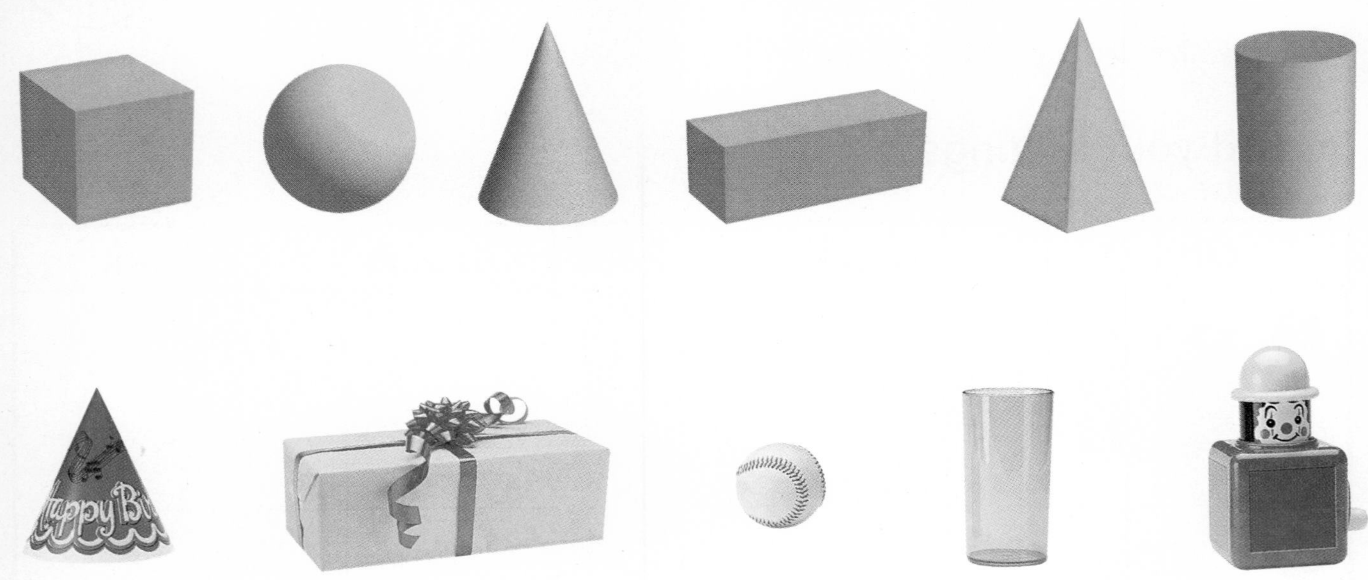

8 Draw your own.

Dear Family: With your child, trace the faces of various objects you have at home. Ask your child to name solids with faces like the ones he or she has traced.

Name____

Surprising Animals

1. Move counters and cutouts to show the stories.
Paste cutouts on the page to show your favorite story.

Count and record how many of each item you see.
Tape cutouts over some of the items. How many are left?

2 

_____ have hats.

_____ have no hats.

_____ still have hats.

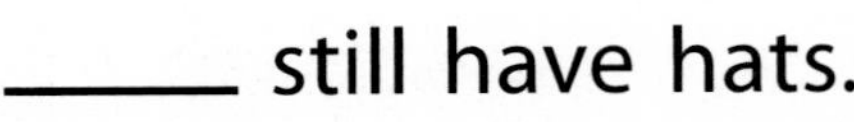

3 

_____ have bows.

_____ have no bows.

_____ still have bows.

4   

_____ have ties.

_____ have no ties.

_____ still have ties.

Dear Family: Point out to your child occasions when part of a group of items is taken away. Take turns asking each other, "How many are left?"

Use these cutouts with pages 43 and 44.

page 44

page 43

Name ______________________________

Parts and Wholes

Color the parts to match the numbers.

1
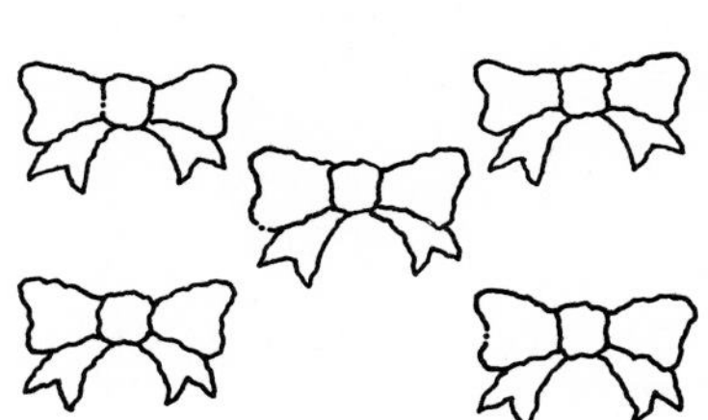
3 + 2

2

2 + 3

3

4 + 1

4

1 + 4

Draw the missing parts.

5

8 flowers

6

10 invitations

7

7 balloons

8

5 pinwheels

Draw the missing parts.
Write the missing number.

9 

4 + 2 = 6

10 

2 + ____ = 8

11 

1 + ____ = 5

12 

5 + ____ = 7

13 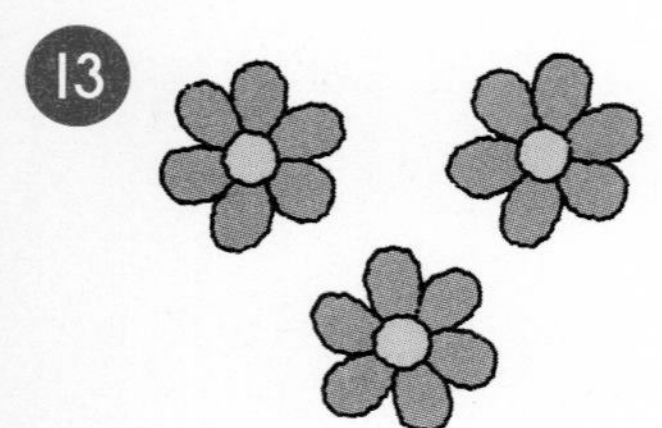

3 + ____ = 3

14 Draw your own.

____ + ____ = ____

Dear Family: Show your child one to nine items. Then ask your child how many you put in your pocket and how many you put in your hand.

Name ______________________________

Measuring with Cubes

Use 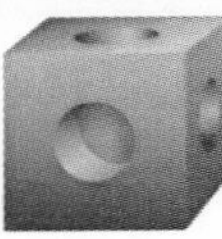 to measure each item.

1 

____ cubes

2 

____ cubes

3 

____ cubes

4 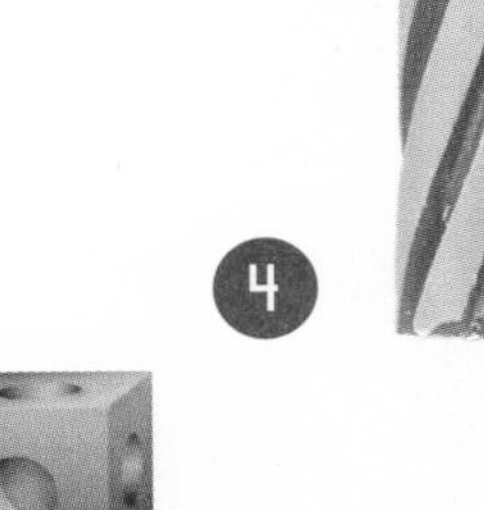

____ 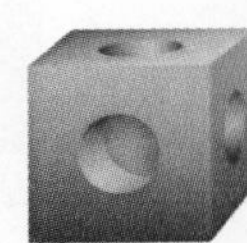

5 

____ 

6 

____ 

7 

____ 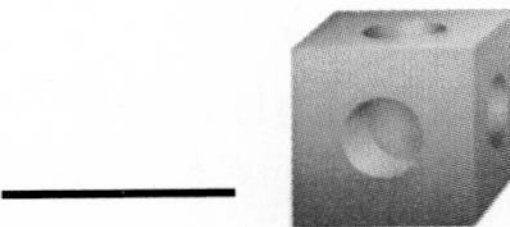

Draw an object about this length.
Then measure its actual length.

Object	Actual Length
8 8  cubes	 ____ cubes
9 10 cubes 	 ____ cubes
10 15 cubes 	 ____ cubes
11 20 cubes 	 ____ cubes

Dear Family: Practice measuring with your child by lining up small items (such as cotton swabs) next to a large object. Then count the smaller items.

Name ______________________________

Comparing with Cubes

Use  to measure the objects below.
Then compare the lengths.

1

a. ____ cubes

b. ____ cubes

Which is longer? ____ How much longer? ____ cubes

2

a. ____ cubes

b. ____ cubes

Which is longer? ____ How much longer? ____ cubes

3

a. ____ cubes

b. ____ cubes

Which is longer? ____ How much longer? ____ 

Estimate length and then measure.

Item	Unit	Estimate	Actual Length
4			
5			
6			
7			
8			

Dear Family: Encourage your child to compare the lengths of two objects by measuring each one with the same measurement unit.

Name ______________________________

Who Am I?

Letters in My Name

A	L	F	O	N	S	O		
M	E	G						
T	A	K	E	O				
J	O	H	N					
A	R	I	E	L				
R	O	S	A	L	I	N	D	A

0 1 2 3 4 5 6 7 8 9

Use the graph and clues to answer the questions.

1. My name has more than 4 letters.
   My name has fewer than 8 letters.
   My name does not start with the letter A.

   Who am I? ______________________

2. My name has fewer than 6 letters.
   My name has more than 3 letters.
   My name does not have the letter E in it.

   Who am I? ______________________

3 Shade a square each time you use a letter.

Dear Family: Use a grid like the one above to help your child graph the letters in the names of members of your household.

Name ____________________

Graph the Games

Shade the graph to show each game item.

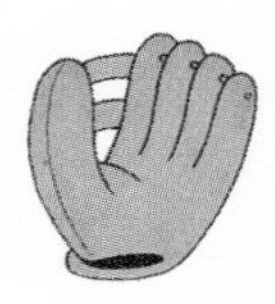

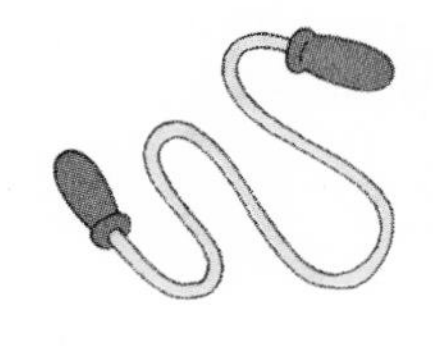

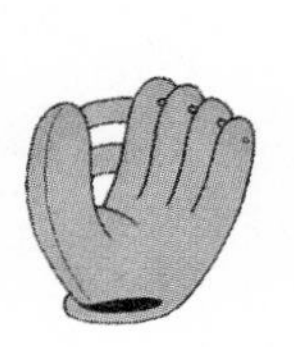

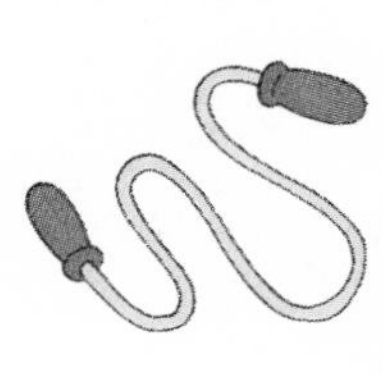

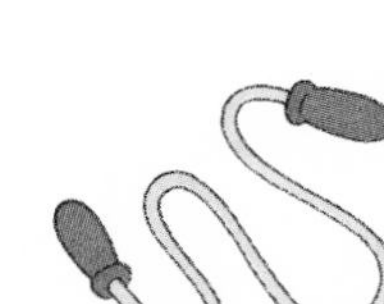

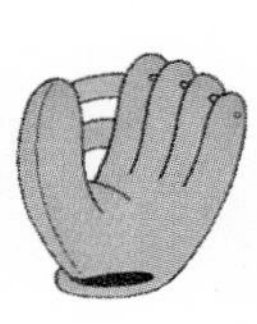

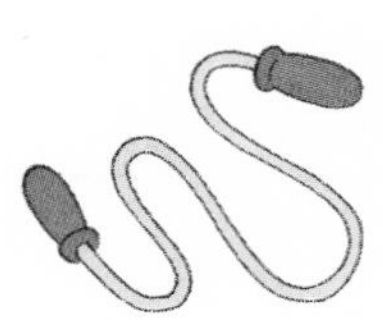

Game Items

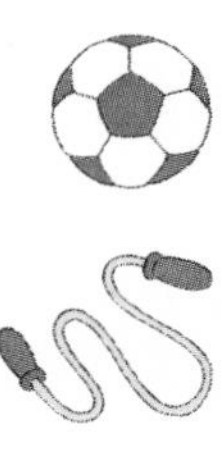

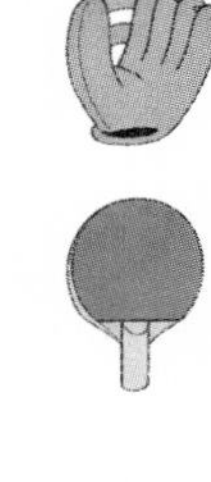

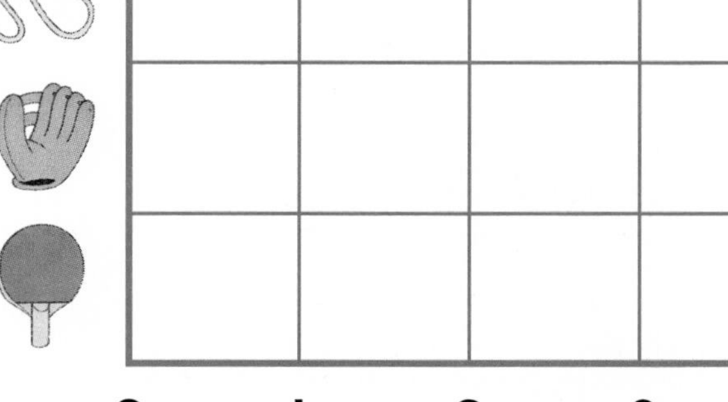

0 1 2 3 4 5

1. How many baseball gloves? ____
2. What do we have the most of? ____________________
3. What do we have the fewest of? ____________________

Use the grid to tell where each child is hiding.

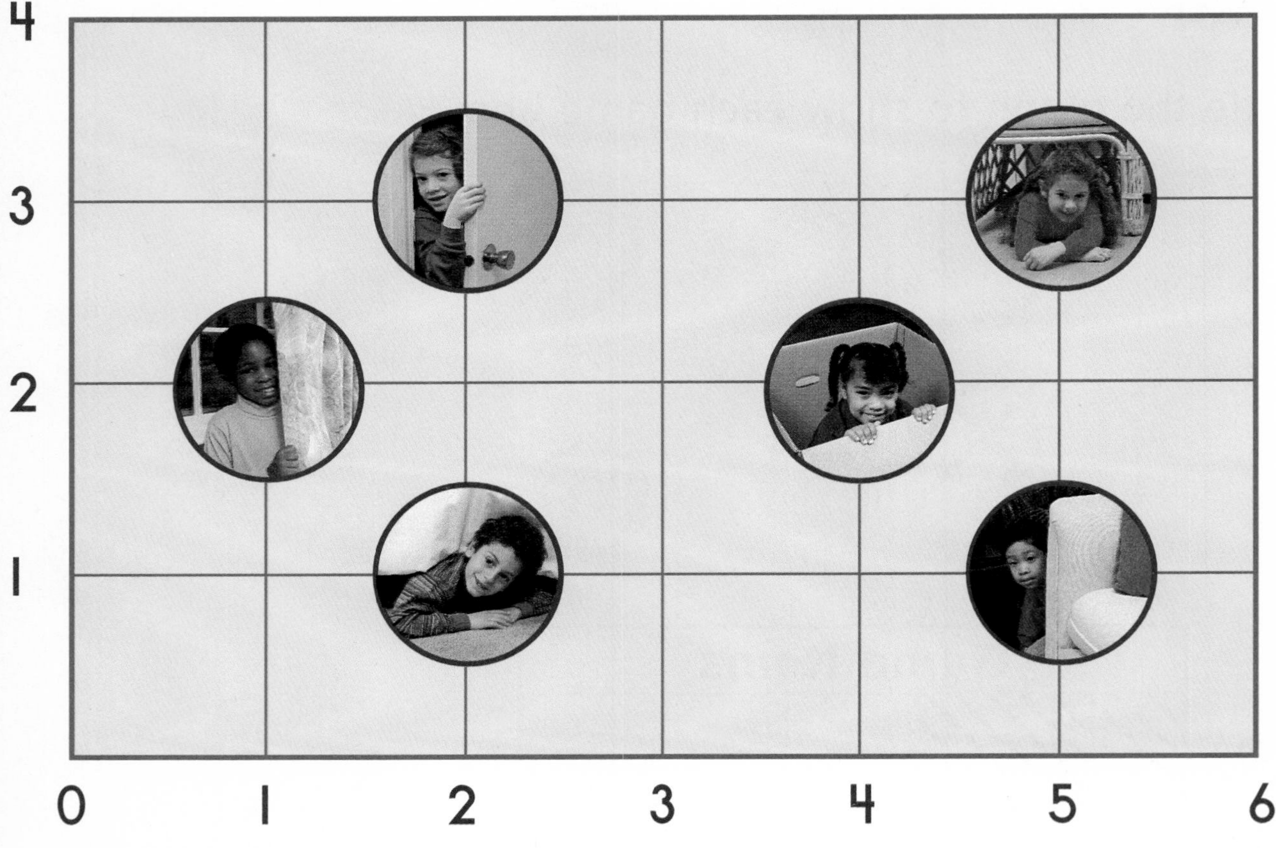

		Across	Up
4		2	3
5			
6			

		Across	Up
7			
8			
9			

Dear Family: Work with your child to create a grid of a room in your home. Describe the location of furniture or objects in the room with pairs of numbers.

Name ______________________________

Subtraction Games

Listen to the stories.
Act them out.

Write a number sentence to go with each story.

1 ____ - ____ = ____ 2 ____ - ____ = ____

Listen to the game rules.

		1	0	3	0	2
START		0				0
1		2		FINISH		1
0		0		0		0
2		3	0	1		4
0						0
3	0	1	0	2	0	3

3. 10 ___ - ___ = ___
4. ___ - ___ = ___
5. ___ - ___ = ___
6. ___ - ___ = ___

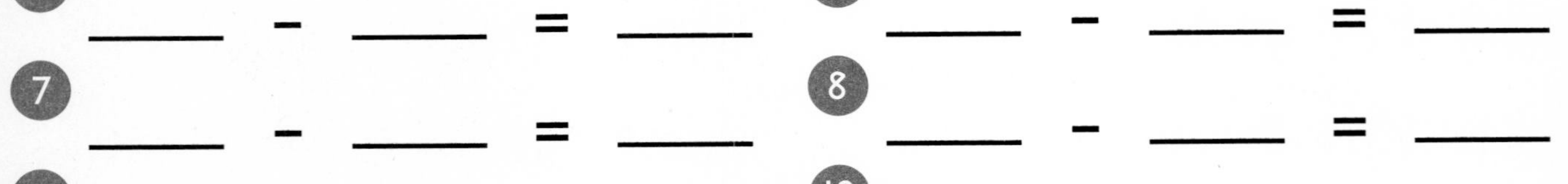

7. ___ - ___ = ___
8. ___ - ___ = ___
9. ___ - ___ = ___
10. ___ - ___ = ___
11. ___ - ___ = ___
12. ___ - ___ = ___
13. ___ - ___ = ___
14. ___ - ___ = ___

Dear Family: Play the game above with your child. You can use dimes or other small objects as counters.

Name ____________________

How Many Are Left?

Listen. Write the number sentence.

1 

____ – ____ = ____

2 

____ – ____ = ____

3 

____ – ____ = ____

4 

____ – ____ = ____

5 

____ – ____ = ____

6 

____ – ____ = ____

Roll a number cube.
Cross out that number of items.
Write the subtraction sentence.

7

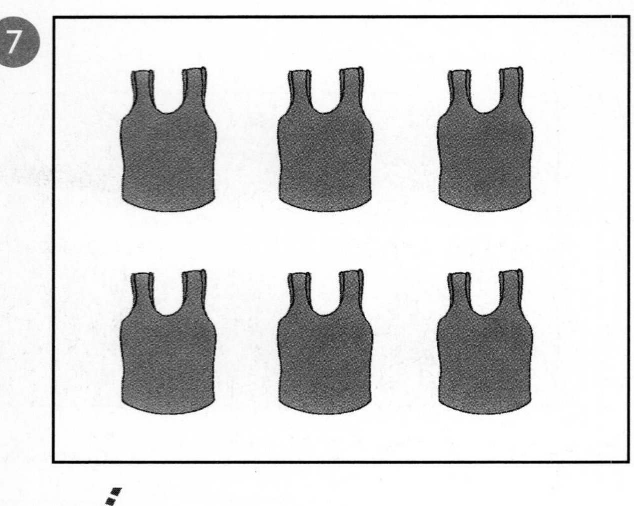

6 – ___ = ___

8

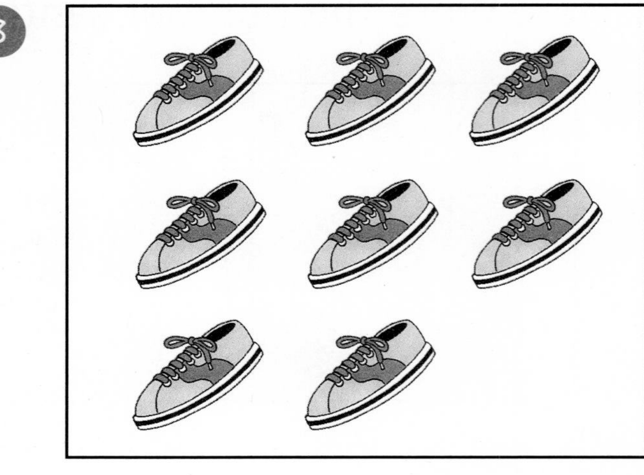

___ – ___ = ___

9

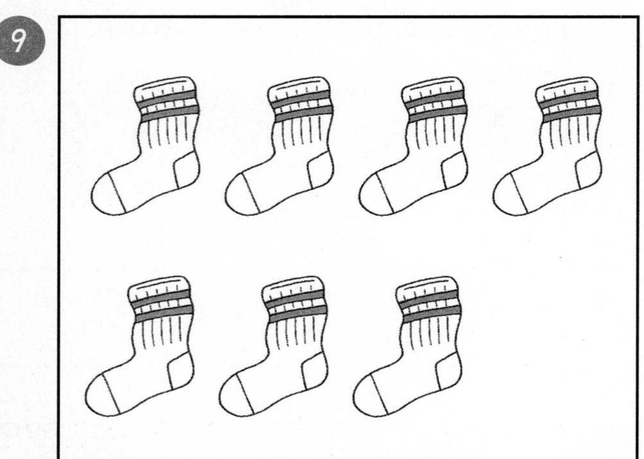

___ – ___ = ___

10

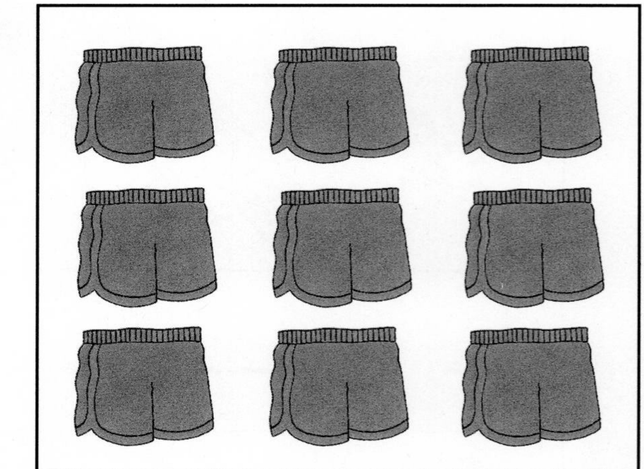

___ – ___ = ___

Dear Family: Find groups of ten or fewer objects in your home. Separate each group into two parts and help your child state the subtraction sentence.

Name ____________________

Shapes and Straws

Take all the △.
Take away the red ▲.

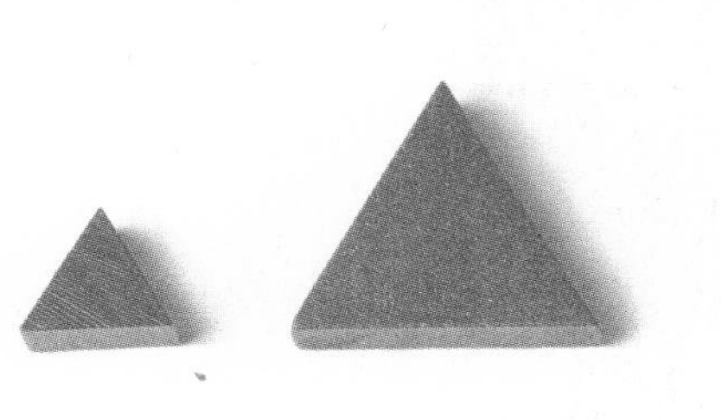

Write a number sentence.  8 – 2 = 6

Model with blocks. Write the number sentence.

1. Take all the ○.
   Take away the red 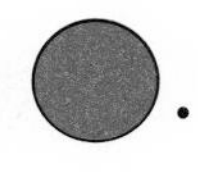. ____ – ____ = ____
2. Take the blue ■.
   Add the green ■. ____ + ____ = ____
3. Take all the ○.
   Take away the small ○. ____ – ____ = ____
   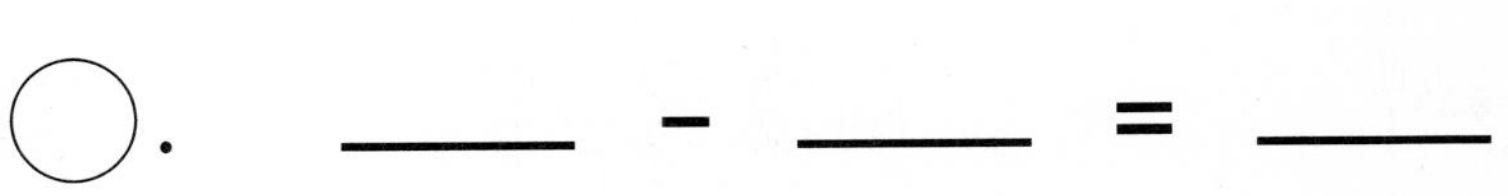
4. Take the small △.
   Add the big △. ____ + ____ = ____
5. Take the yellow ▱.
   Add the small □. ____ + ____ = ____

Play pick-up straws.
Write a subtraction sentence after each try.

6. 10 − ____ = ____

7. ____ − ____ = ____

8. ____ − ____ = ____

9. ____ − ____ = ____

10. ____ − ____ = ____

11. ____ − ____ = ____

12. ____ − ____ = ____

13. ____ − ____ = ____

14. ____ − ____ = ____

15. How many tries did you need to pick up all the straws? ____

Dear Family: With your child, think of ways to separate items, such as groceries, into two groups. Then write subtraction sentences to match.

Name ____________________

Make It Match!

Draw shapes or use an X to show the number.
Write the number sentence.

1. Show 5.

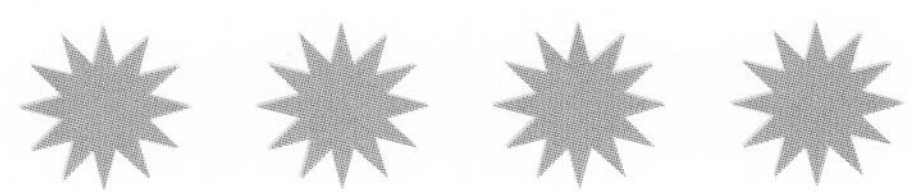

6 – 1 = 5

2. Show 6.

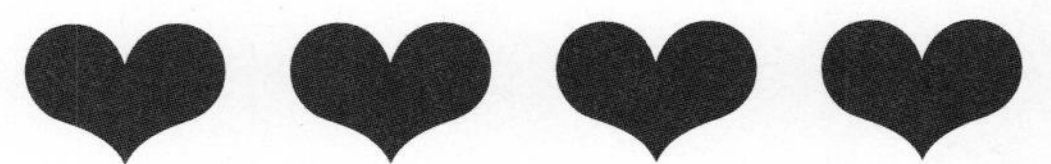

____ + ____ = ____

3. Show 7.

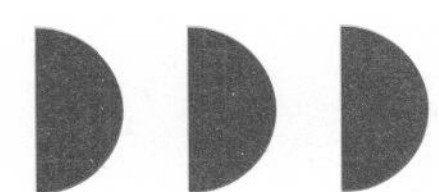

____ + ____ = ____

4. Show 3.

____ – ____ = ____

5. Show 2.

____ – ____ = ____

6. Show 9.

____ + ____ = ____

Draw a picture to show the number sentence.
Write the answer.

7

9 - 7 = ____

8

$$\begin{array}{r} 6 \\ -\ 3 \\ \hline \end{array}$$

9

5 + 1 = ____

10

$$\begin{array}{r} 4 \\ +\ 3 \\ \hline \end{array}$$

11

2 + 3 = ____

12

$$\begin{array}{r} 10 \\ -\ 4 \\ \hline \end{array}$$

Dear Family: Invite your child to model the number sentences above using items such as toys, books, or socks.

Name ____________________

Doing Doubles

Connect the matching socks.

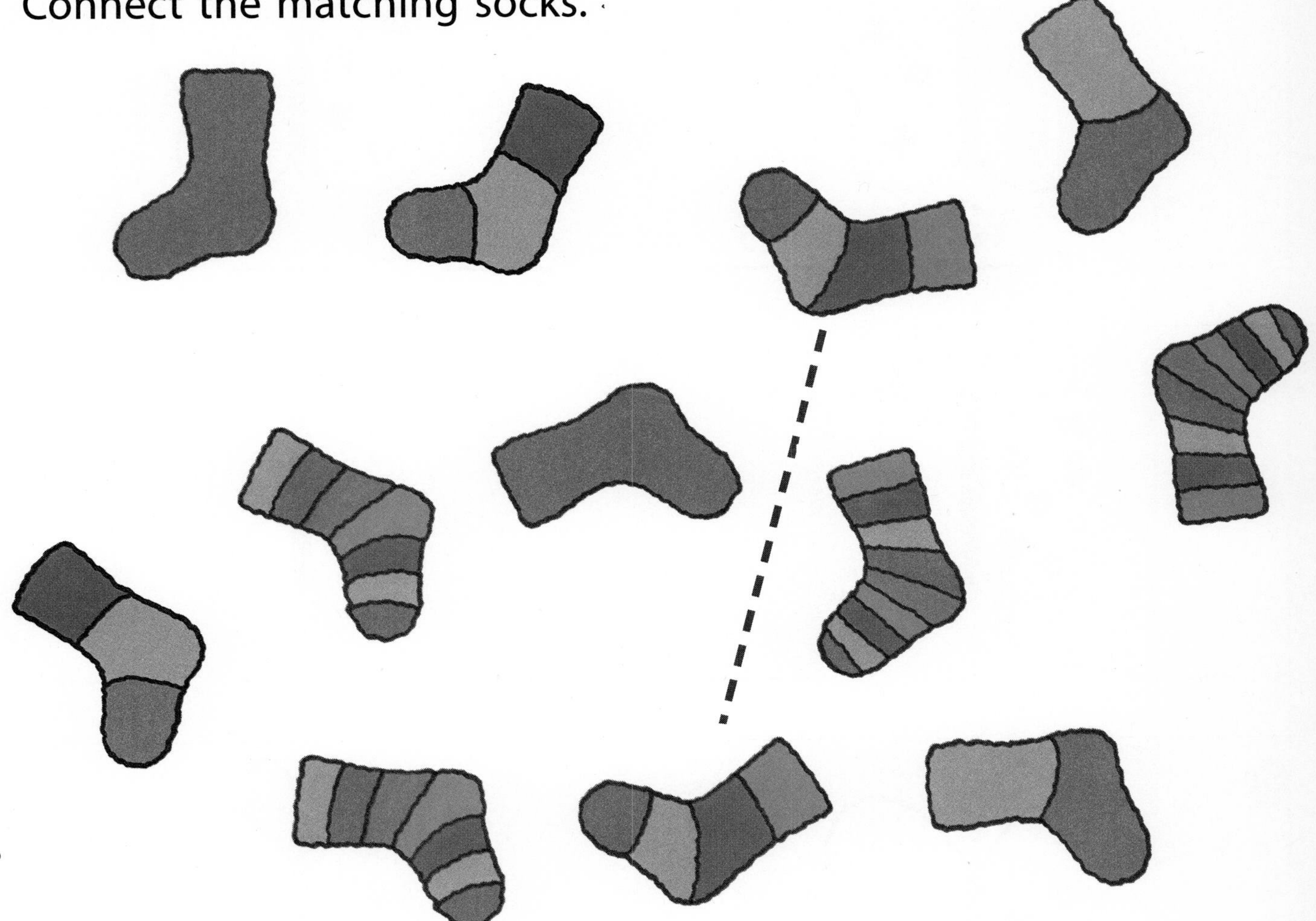

Write the doubles addition sentences.

1. 4 + 4 = 8
2. ____ + ____ = ____
3. ____ + ____ = ____
4. ____ + ____ = ____
5. ____ + ____ = ____
6. ____ + ____ = ____

Add spots to make doubles.
Write the addition sentence.

7

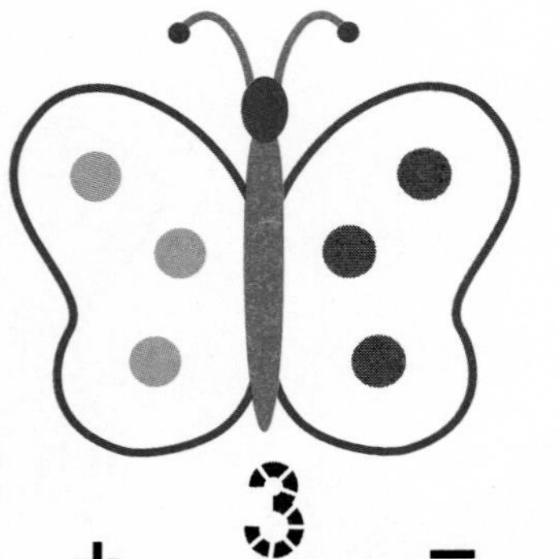

3 + 3 = 6

8

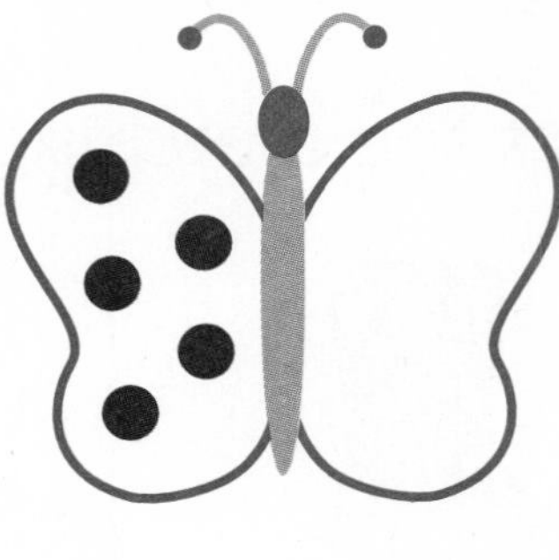

___ + ___ = ___

9

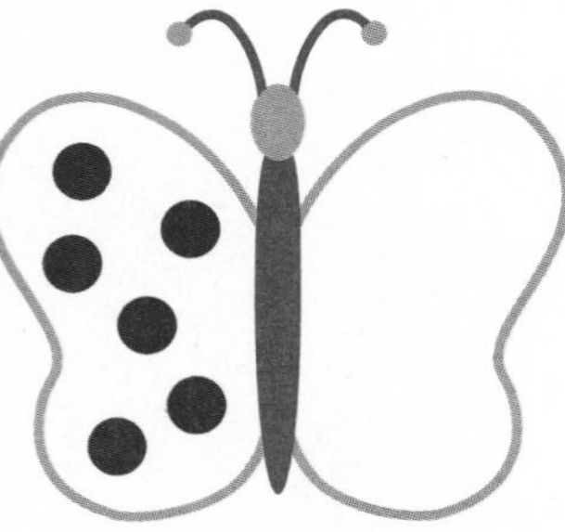

___ + ___ = ___

10

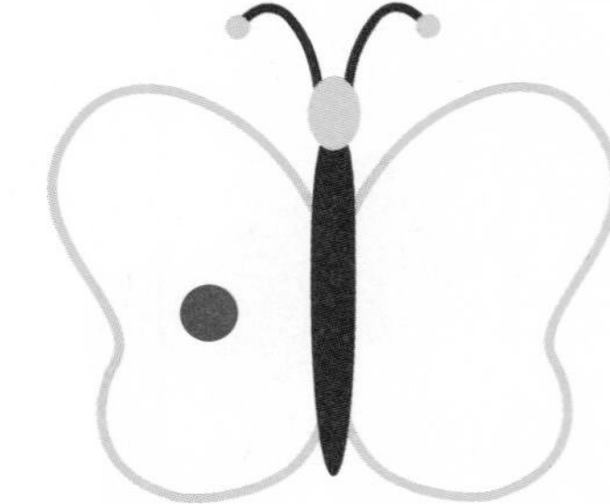

___ + ___ = ___

11

___ + ___ = ___

12

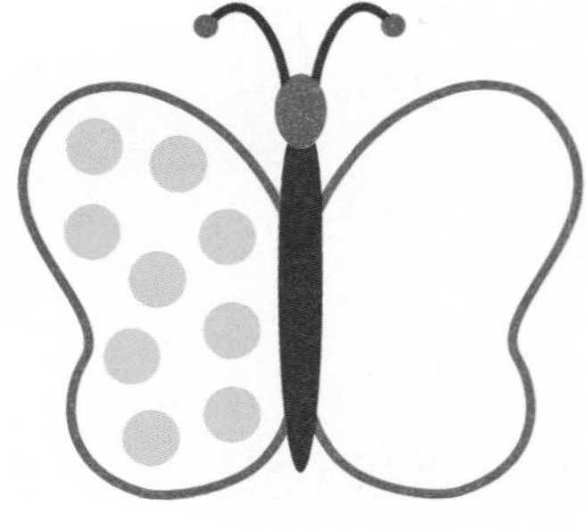

___ + ___ = ___

Dear Family: Play dominoes together. Say the addition sentence for each domino placed.

Name ______________________________

Drawing Doubles

Write how many fish there are.

1

2

___ + ___ = ___   ___ + ___ = ___

Draw fish in the fishbowls.

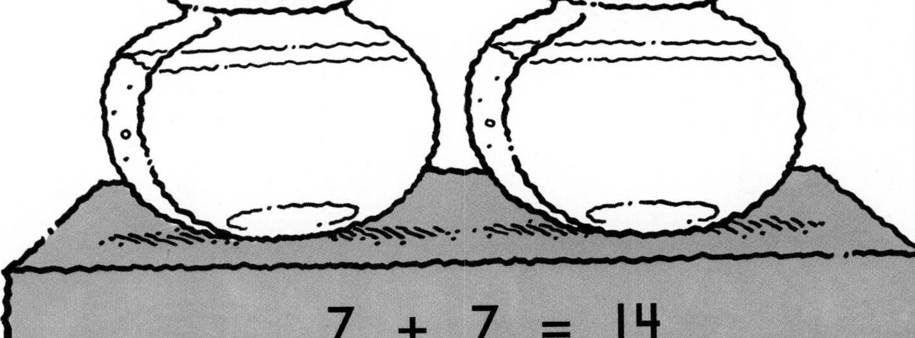

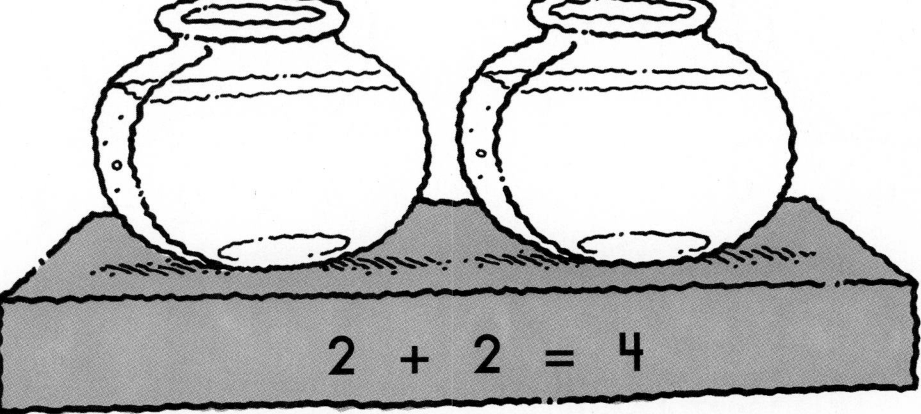

Some fish are moving to a new bowl.
How many fish are left in the bowl?

5

____ - ____ = ____

Draw the fish that are moving to a new bowl.
Draw the fish that are left in the bowl.

6

12 - 6 = 6

7

10 - 5 = 5

8

8 - 4 = 4

9

4 - 2 = 2

Dear Family: Look for games or places where you see doubles.

Name________________________________

Penny Prices

Ring the coins that equal the price shown.

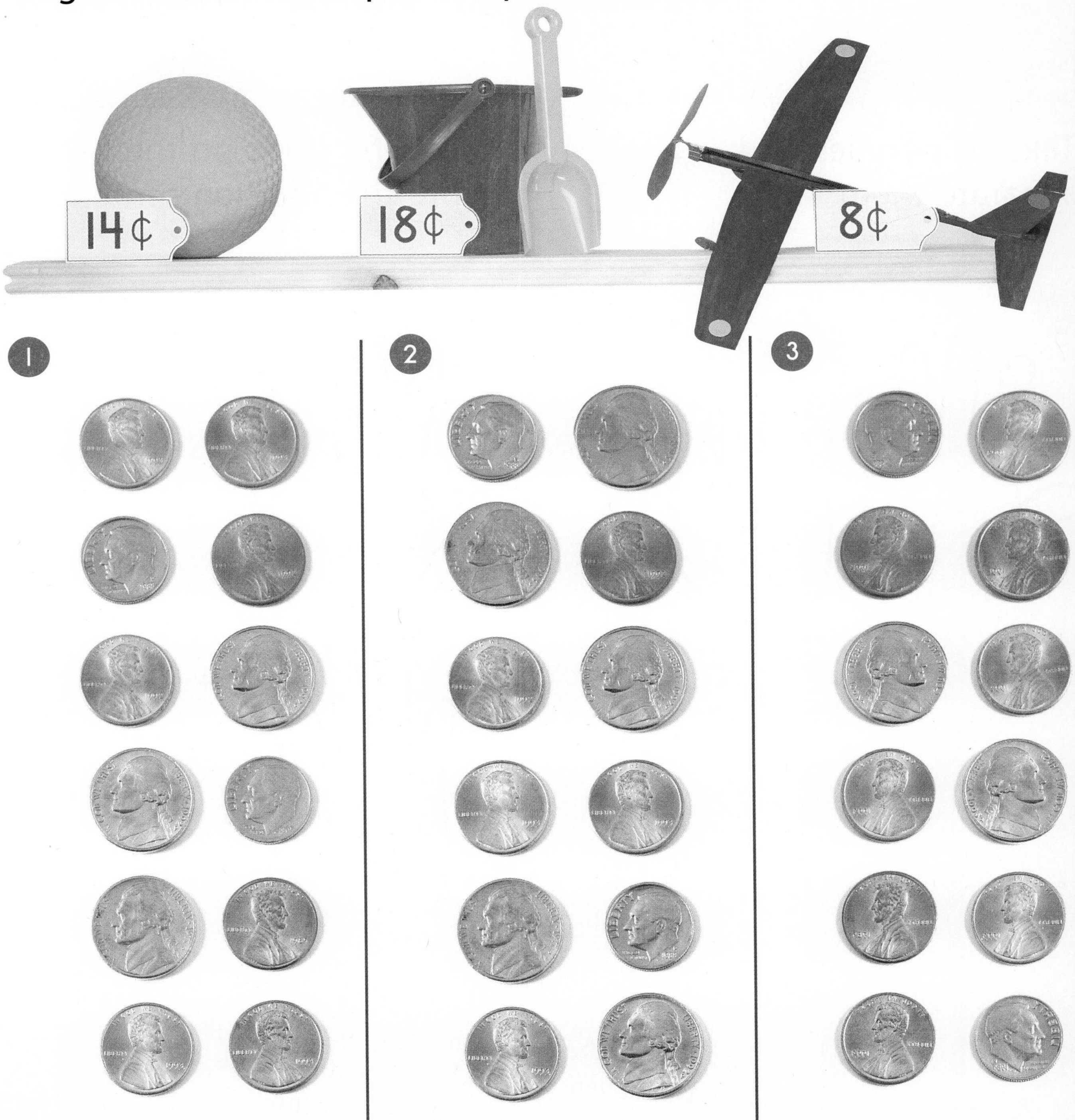

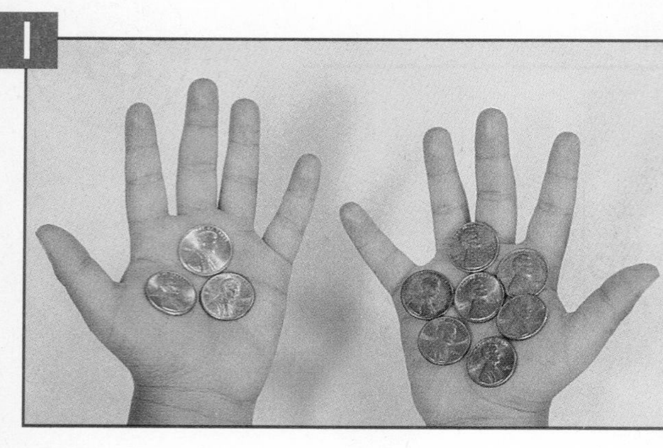

1 Take 10 pennies and separate them.

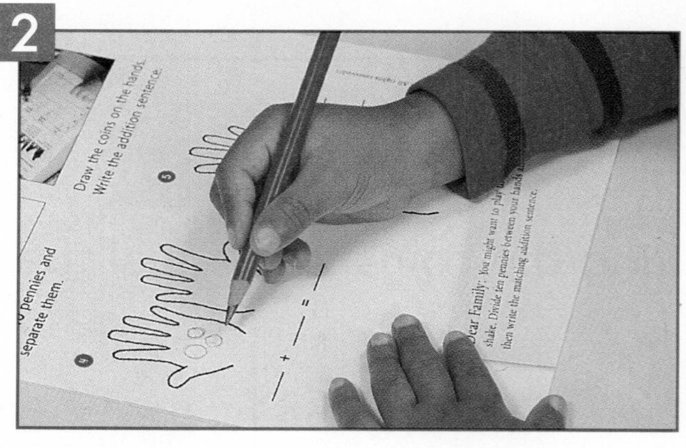

2 Draw the coins on the hands. Write the addition sentence.

4

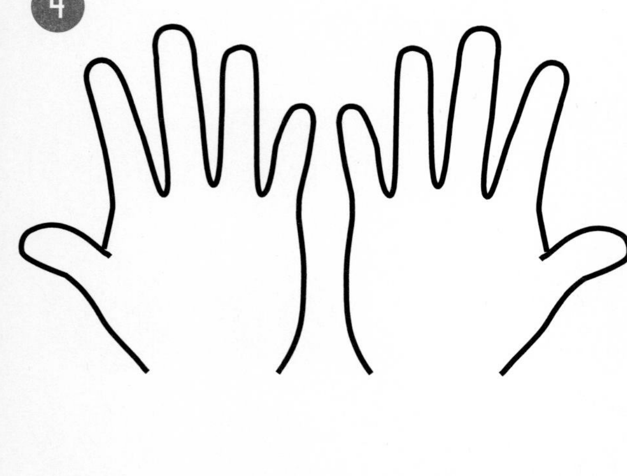

____ + ____ = ____

5

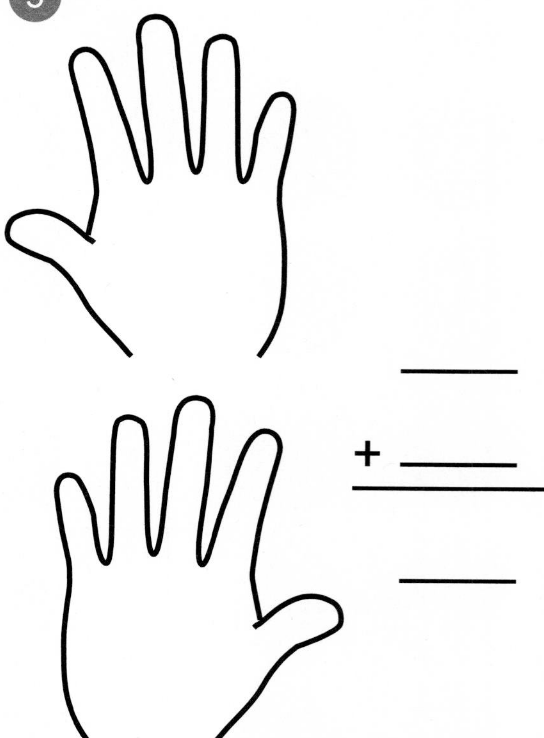

____
+ ____
____

Dear Family: You might want to play the penny shake. Divide ten pennies between your hands and then write the matching addition sentence.

Name ______________________________

How Many Coins?

1 Use coins to buy the items on the list.
Draw the coins you use.

Need to buy:
2 oranges
1 apple

2 oranges	1 apple

1 Draw 10 pennies.

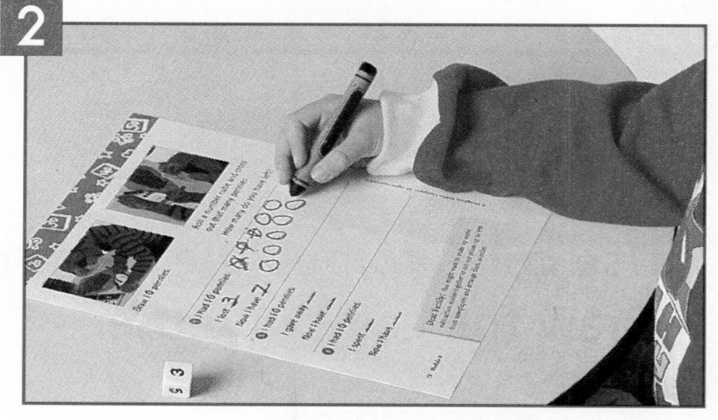

2 Roll a number cube.
Cross out that many pennies.
How many do you have left?

2. I had 10 pennies.

I lost ____.

Now I have ____.

3. I had 10 pennies.

I gave away ____.

Now I have ____.

4. I had 10 pennies.

I spent ____.

Now I have ____.

Dear Family: You might want to make up some subtraction stories together or cut out prices up to 99¢ from newspapers and arrange them in order.

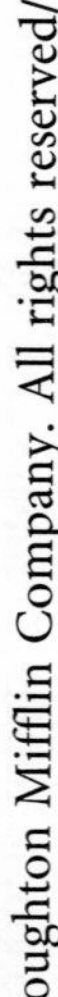

Name____

Hat Counting

Tally.
Write the numbers.

Hat	Tally	Number
1		
2		
3		

Draw more to make 10.
Write the number.

4

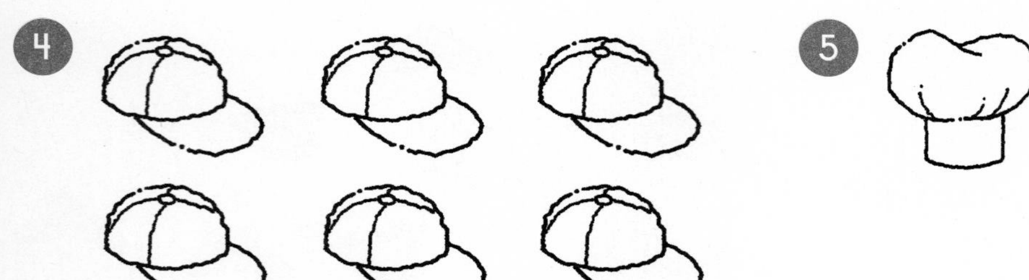

5

6 + ____ = 10

1 + ____ = 10

6

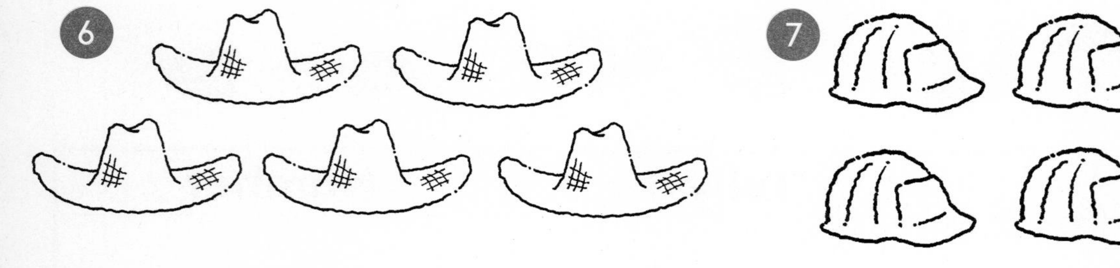

7

5 + ____ = 10

8 + ____ = 10

Dear Family: Ask your child to help you set the table. Practice making addition sentences by asking, "How many more forks would we need to make ten?"

Name ______________________________

Bead Counts

Estimate, tally, and count the beads.
Write the number.

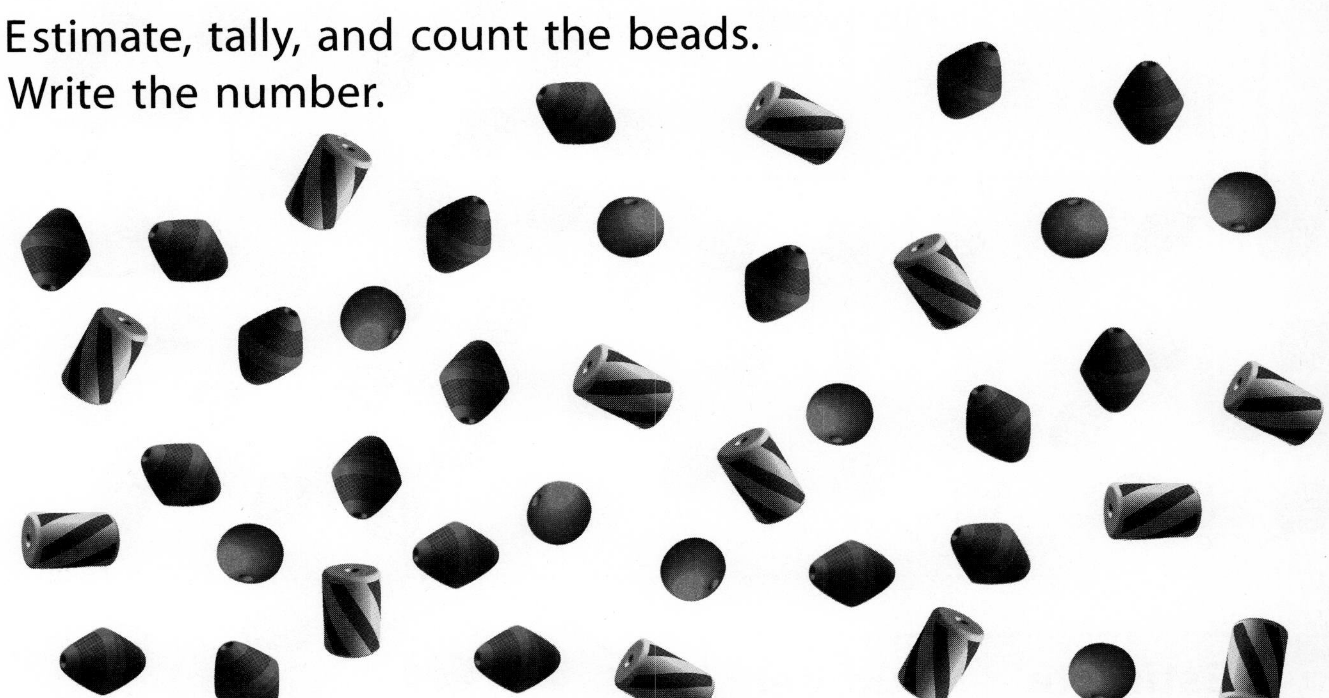

Bead	Estimate	Tally	Number
1			
2			
3			

Estimate and count the beads.
Write the number.

4

Estimate	Number

5

Estimate	Number

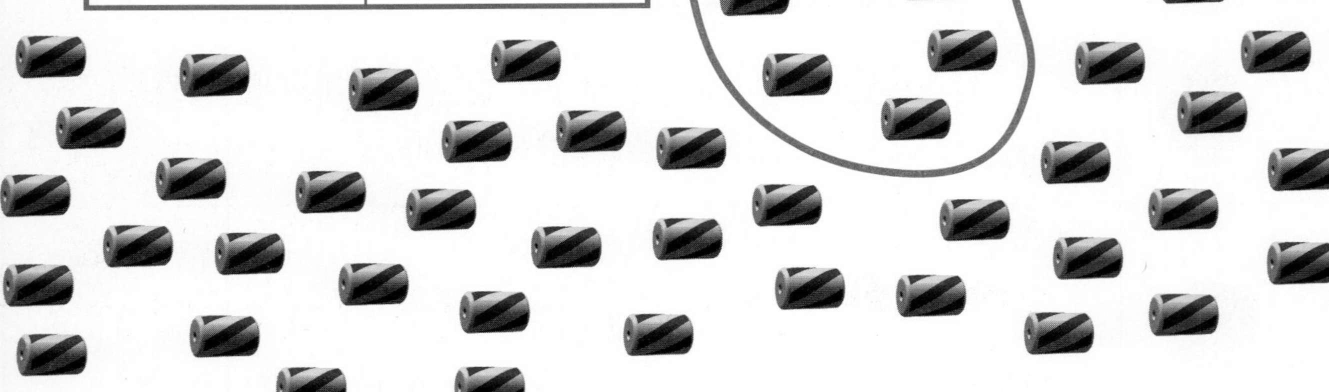

Dear Family: Talk with your child about where he or she sees numbers that are organized, such as on a hopscotch board or a calendar.

Name ____________________

Counting Tens and Ones

Ring ten.
Write the tens and ones.
Write the total.

1

Tens	Ones

______

2

Tens	Ones

______

3

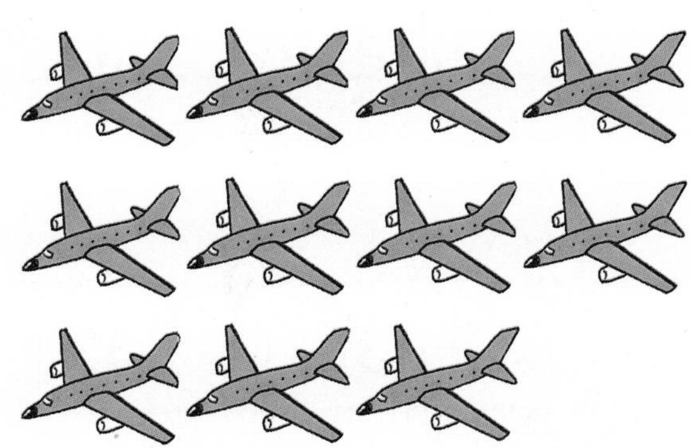

Tens	Ones

______

4

Tens	Ones

______

Count the tens and ones.
Write the total.

5

Tens	Ones

____

6

Tens	Ones

____

7

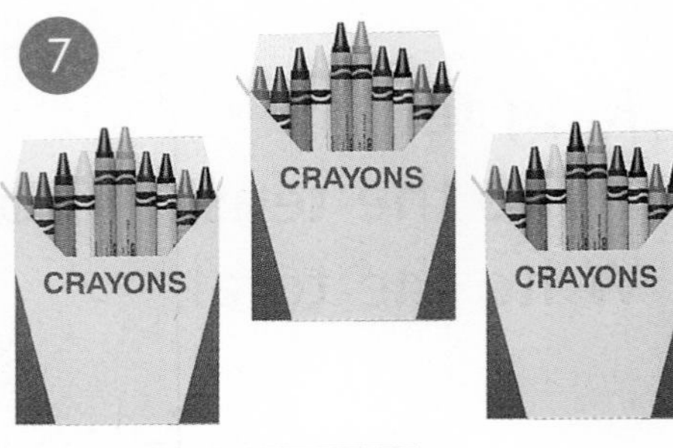

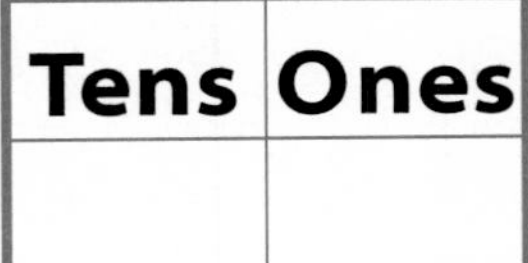

Tens	Ones

____

8

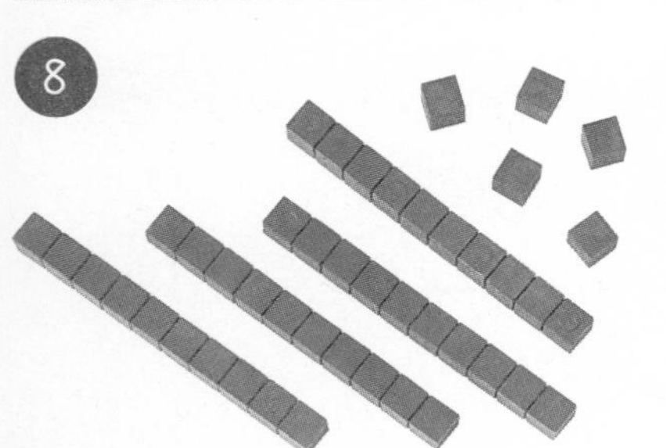

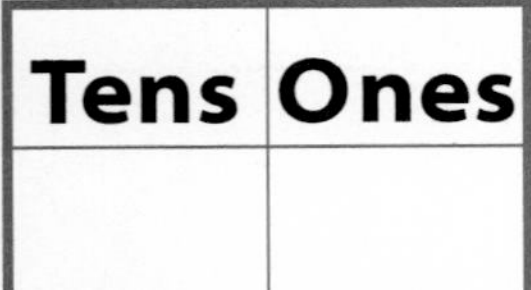

Tens	Ones

____

9

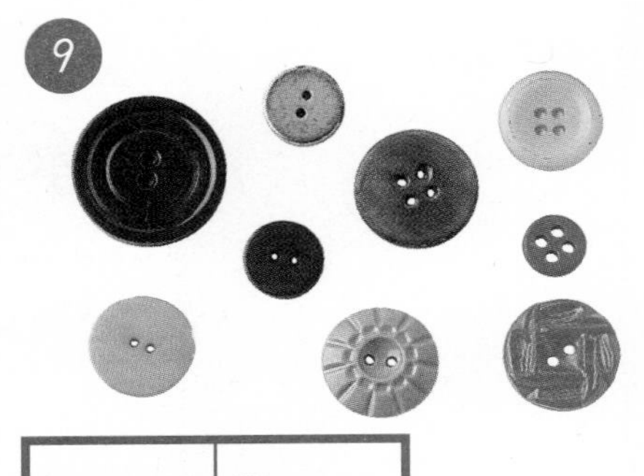

Tens	Ones

____

10

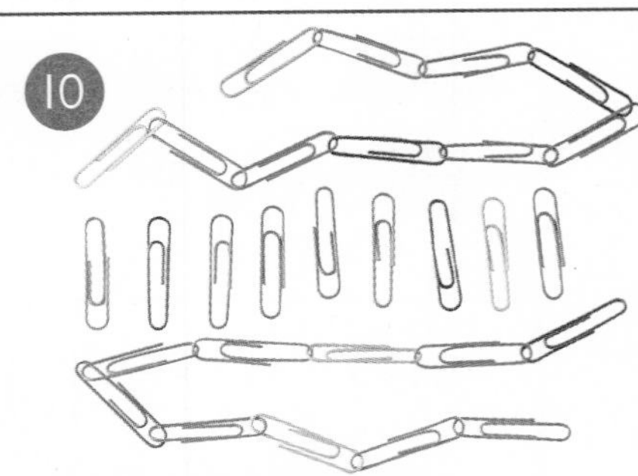

Tens	Ones

____

11 Fill in the missing numbers.

22	23		25			28		30	31		33	

Dear Family: With your child collect 11–99 similar small objects, such as rubber bands or pieces of pasta. Then group them and count the tens and ones.

Name ________________________________

Counting and Ordering

Write the tens and ones. Write the total.

1

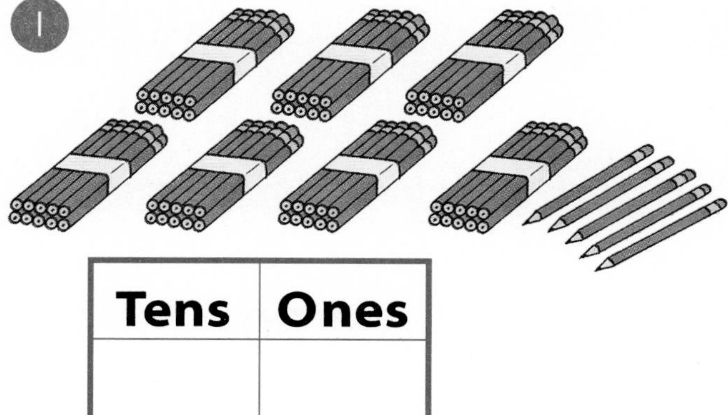

Tens	Ones

______

2

Tens	Ones

______

3

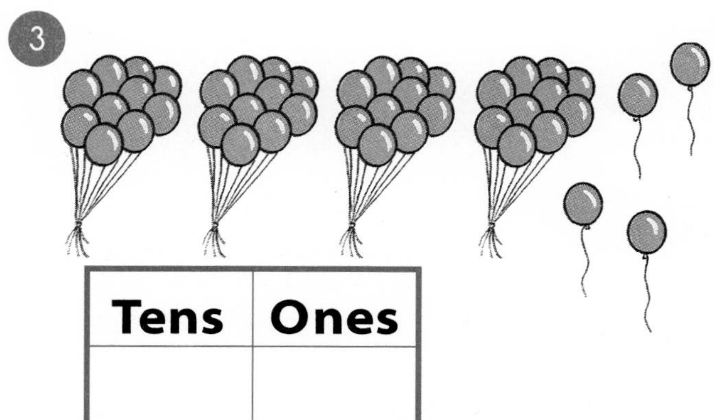

Tens	Ones

______

4

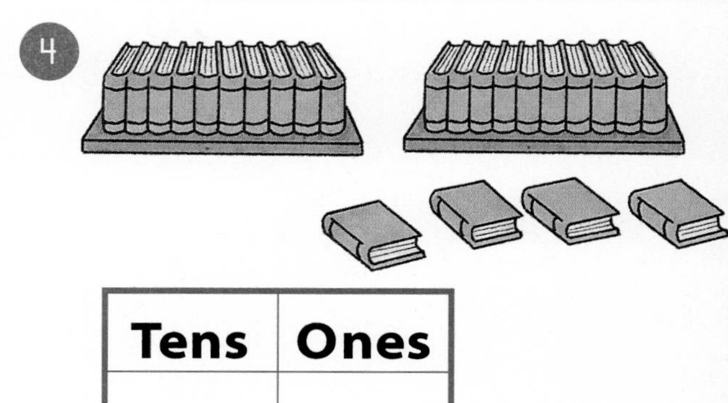

Tens	Ones

______

5

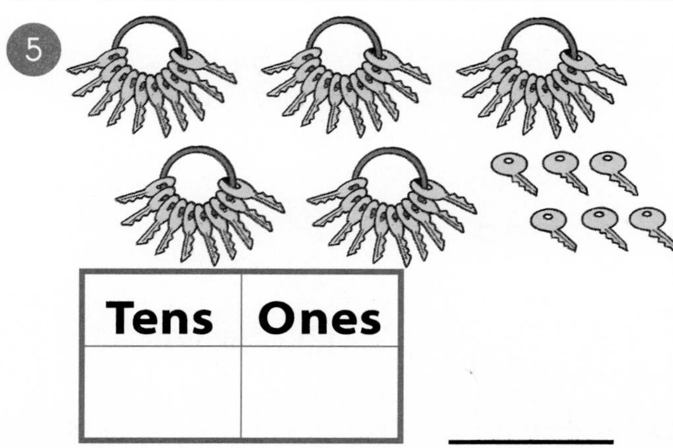

Tens	Ones

______

6

Tens	Ones

______

Draw three more.
Place the numbers in order on your drawings.

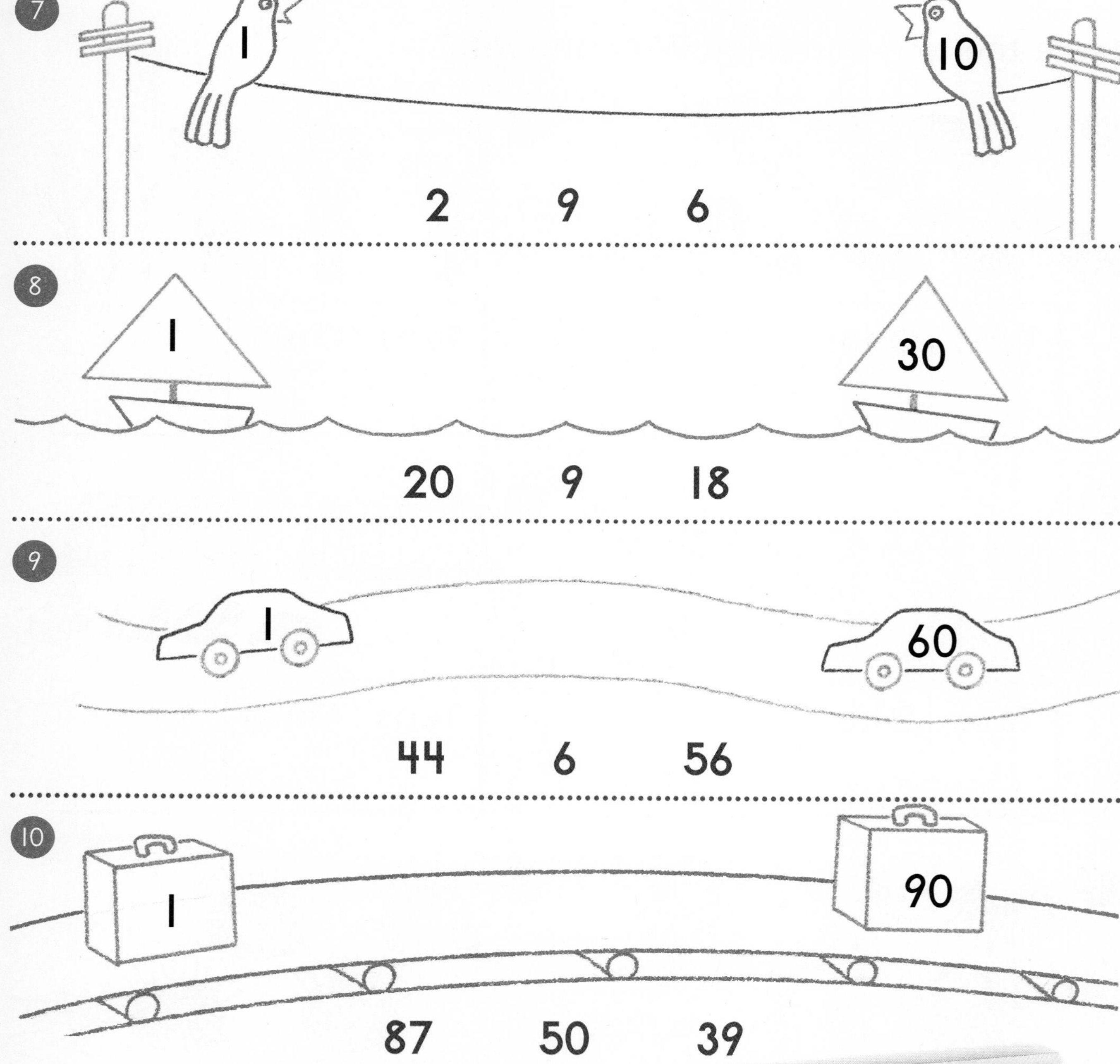

Dear Family: Whenever you and your child encounter a series of three or more numbers, ask which is greatest and which is least.

Name ________________________________

Counting Coins

Write the number of coins that you need.

1. For lunch I need _____ dimes and _____ pennies.
2. For fruit I need _____ dimes and _____ pennies.
3. For a book I need _____ dimes and _____ pennies.
4. At Funland I need _____ dimes and _____ pennies.
5. In all I need _____ dimes and _____ pennies.
6. Write the total. _____ ¢

7 Ring coins that make 10¢.

8 Write the total amount. ____ ¢

Dear Family: Gather some change from around your home and work with your child to arrange groups of ten cents. Use the groups to help count the total.

Name____

How Can You Pay for It?

Connect each group of coins with the right price.

1 

2 

3 

4 

Show three ways to pay for each toy.
Write the number of each coin used.

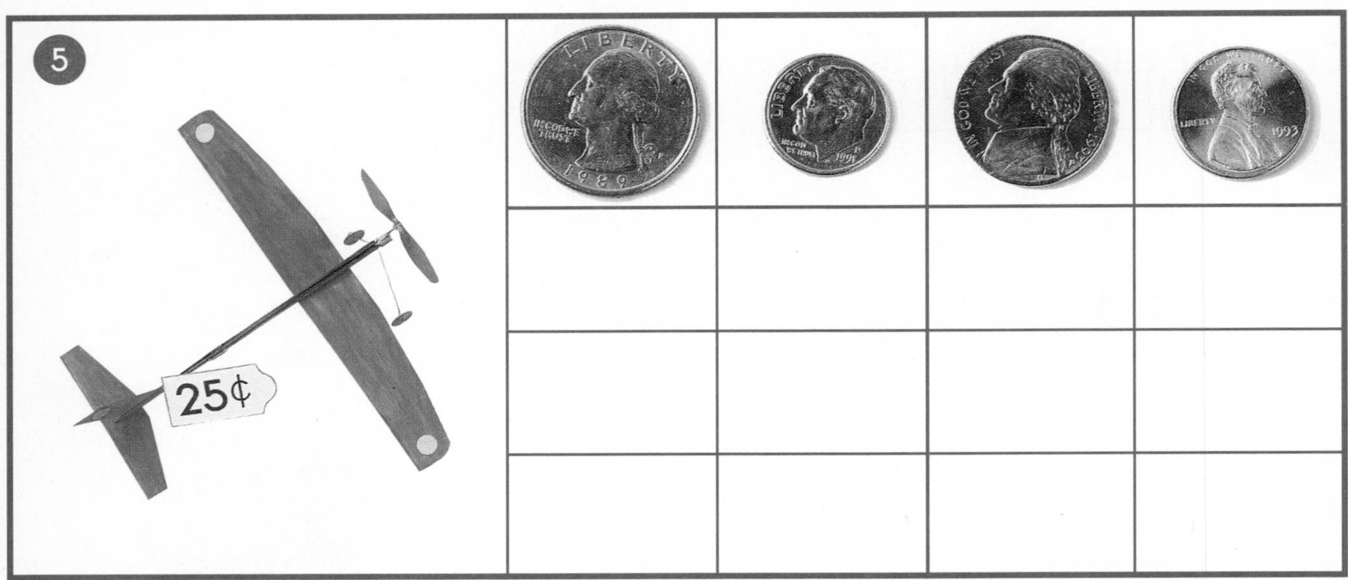

Dear Family: The next time you pay for something, ask your child to help you decide which coins to use.

Name ________________________________

How Long Is It?

Measure each item with your centimeter ruler.

1 

_____ centimeters

2 

_____ centimeters

3 I ♥ ART

_____ centimeters

4 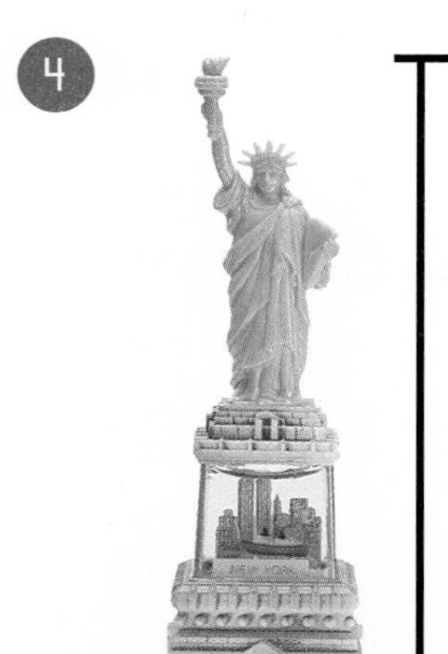

_____ centimeters

5 Draw and measure a small item of your choice.

_____ centimeters

Estimate the length.
Then measure and record it.

	Estimate	Measure
6	____ centimeters	____ centimeters
7	____ centimeters	____ centimeters
8 BOSTON	____ centimeters	____ centimeters
9	____ centimeters	____ centimeters

Dear Family: Spend some time with your child guessing the lengths of various objects around your home and then measuring them in centimeters.

Name ______________________________

How Long Are These Items?

Find the item.
Estimate the length.
Then measure and record it.

1 

Estimate	Measure
____ centimeters	____ centimeters

2 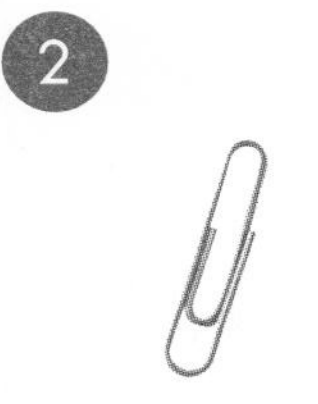

Estimate	Measure
____ centimeters	____ centimeters

3 

Estimate	Measure
____ centimeters	____ centimeters

4 Draw an item.

Estimate	Measure
____ centimeters	____ centimeters

5 Measure these items.

____ centimeters

____ centimeters

____ centimeters

____ centimeters

Dear Family: Ask your child to show you how he or she measures curved objects using a centimeter tape or a piece of string and a centimeter ruler.

Name ______________________________

Same Size and Shape

1 Use attribute blocks.
Find the same size and shape.
Color the shapes to match the drawing.

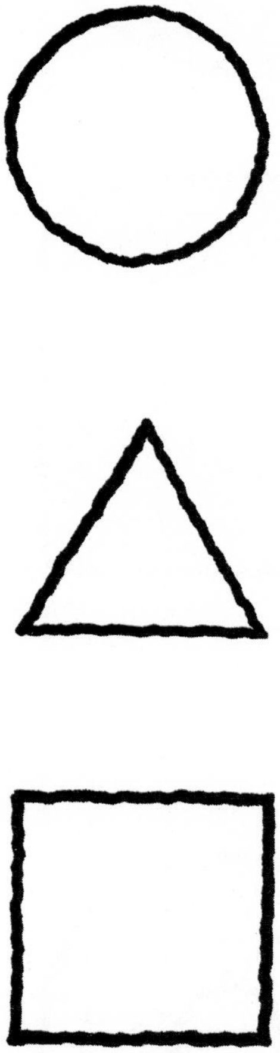

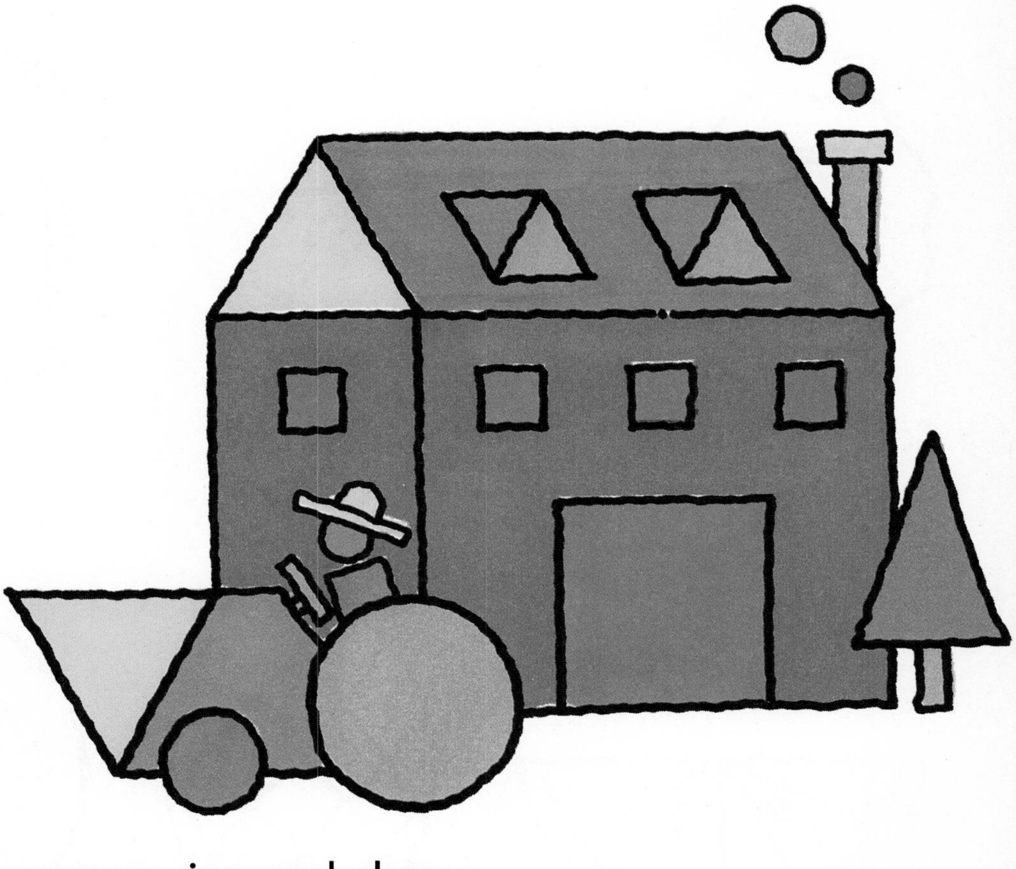

Draw one the same size and shape.

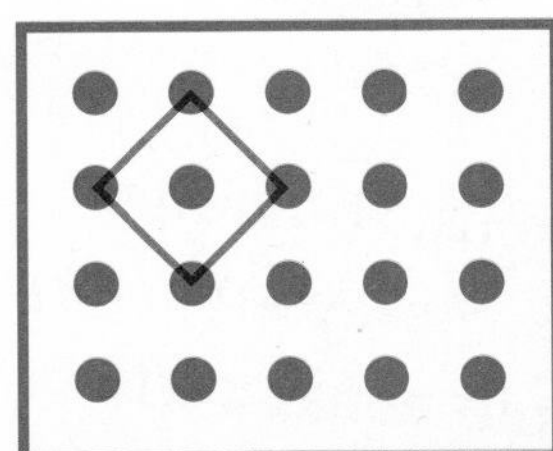

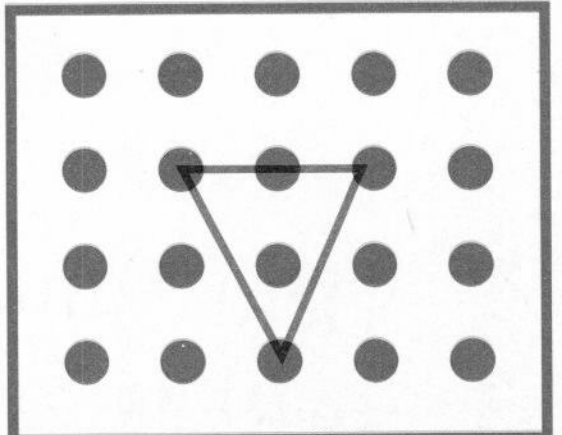

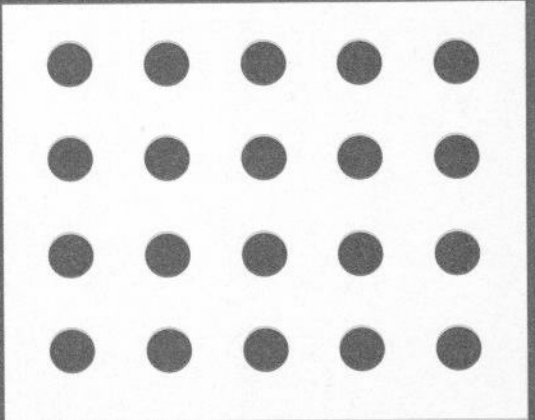

4 Ring the foods that are cut into equal parts.

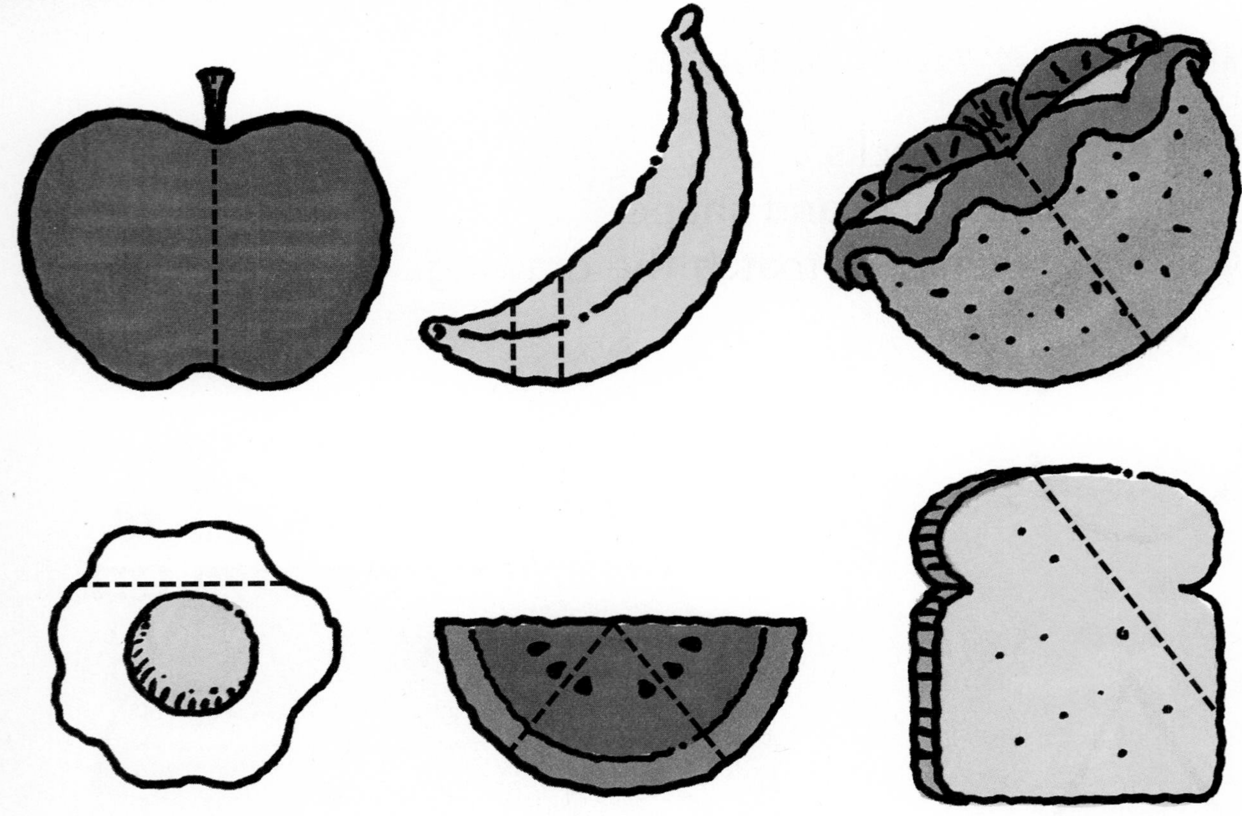

5 Color one half of each food shape.

Dear Family: Slice a variety of food items, some into equal parts and others into unequal parts. Ask your child to select the foods that are divided into equal parts.

Name ______________________________

Shapes and Parts

Ring the circles.
Draw an X on the triangles.
Draw a ✓ on the rectangles.
Draw a square in the picture.

Find the fraction.

1 Ring the object that shows halves. Color one half.

2 Ring the object that shows thirds. Color one third.

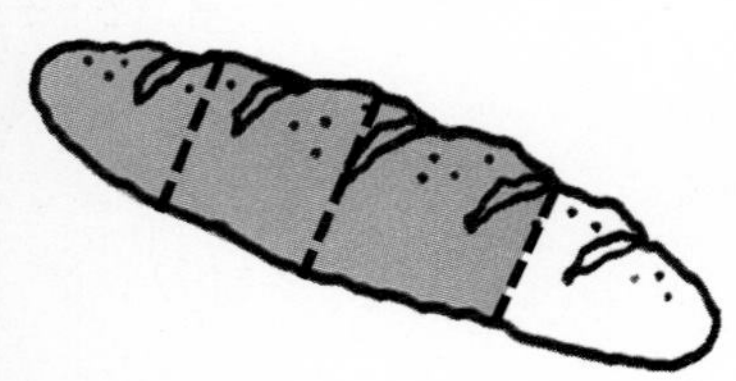

3 Ring the object that shows fourths. Color one fourth.

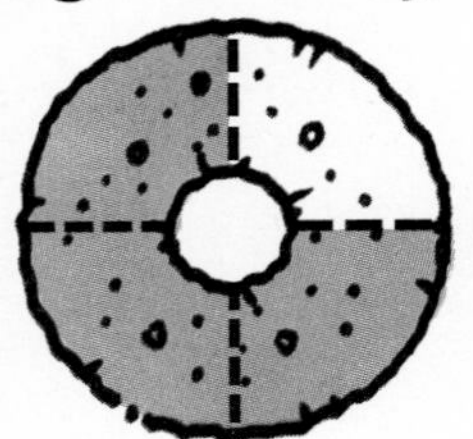

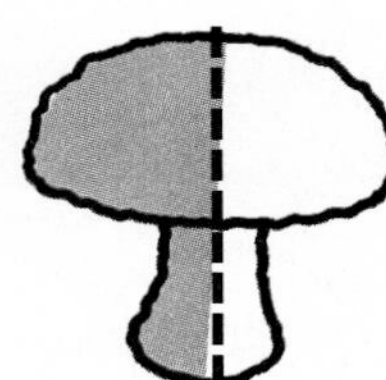

4 How can Bob and Reena share 8 crackers?
Draw crackers in the rings to show.

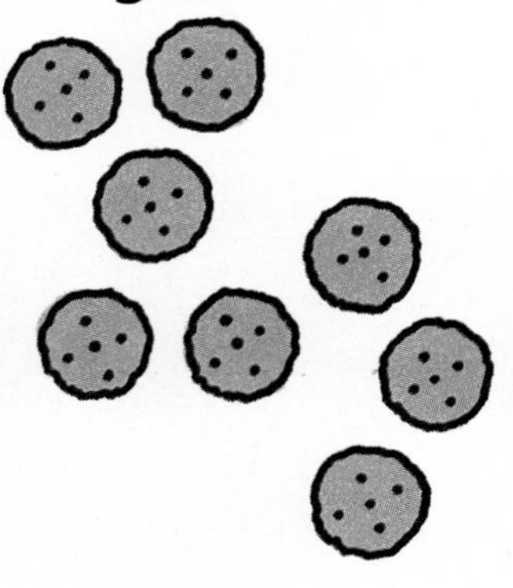

Dear Family: During a meal, talk about food fractions. Divide some food items equally among people. Ask your child to tell the fraction each person gets.

Name ______________________________

How Long Is a Minute?

Take turns doing the activity. Your partner tallies how many you can do in a minute.

1 

Draw triangles. Tally.

Total

2 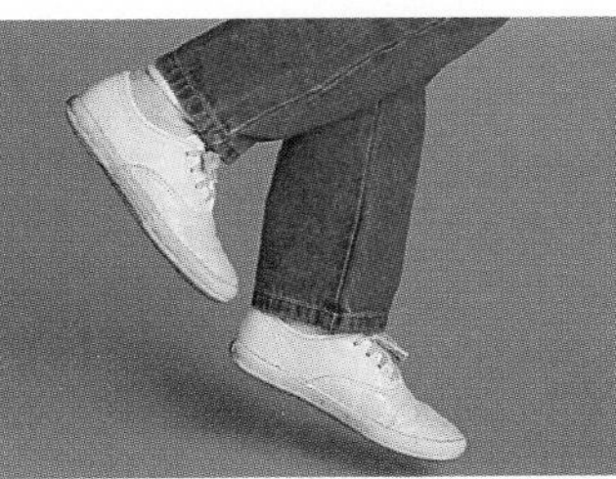

Hop on one foot. Tally.

Total

3 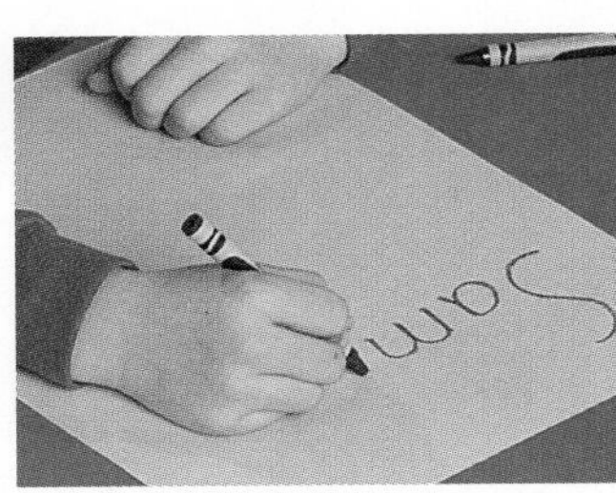

Write your name. Tally.

Total

4 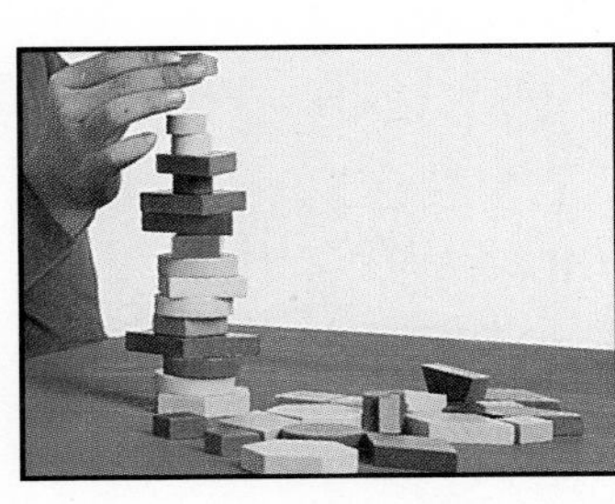

Stack pattern blocks. Tally.

Total

Ring the activity that takes longer than a minute.

5 Make bread. Take a bite.

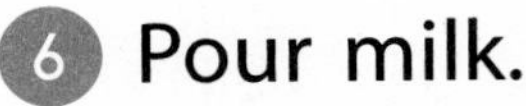

6 Pour milk. Eat lunch.

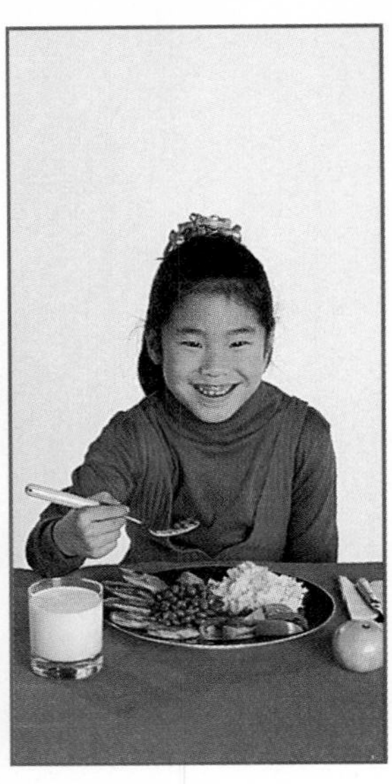

7 Tie your shoe. Walk to school.

8 Build a tower. Knock it down.

Dear Family: With your child, compare the time it takes to do different things around your home. Does it take more time to make a bed or wash the dishes?

Name ______________________________

Time and Temperature

Estimate the temperature.
Color the thermometer.

1 ice cube

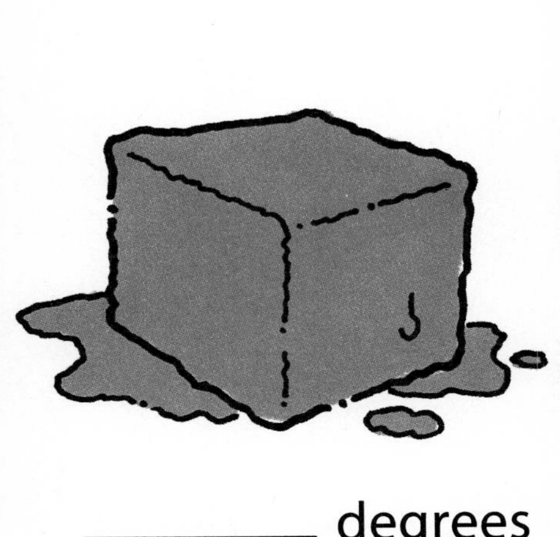

________ degrees

2 baked potato

________ degrees

3 juice bar

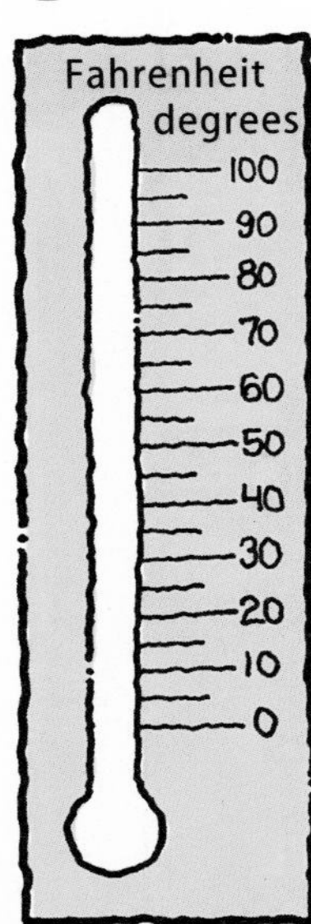

________ degrees

4 rice

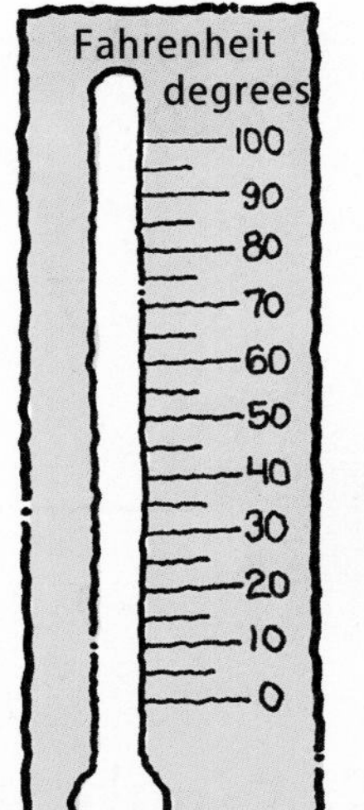

________ degrees

Write or draw the time.

5

_____ o'clock

6

6 o'clock

7

_____ o'clock

8

_____ : _____

9

_____ : _____

10
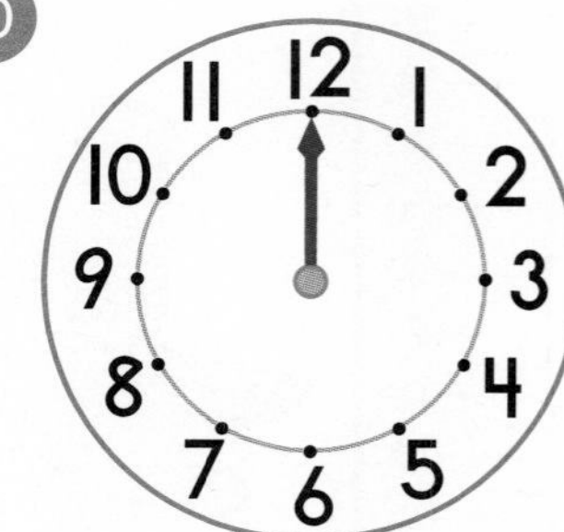

3:00

11

_____ : _____

12

_____ : _____

13
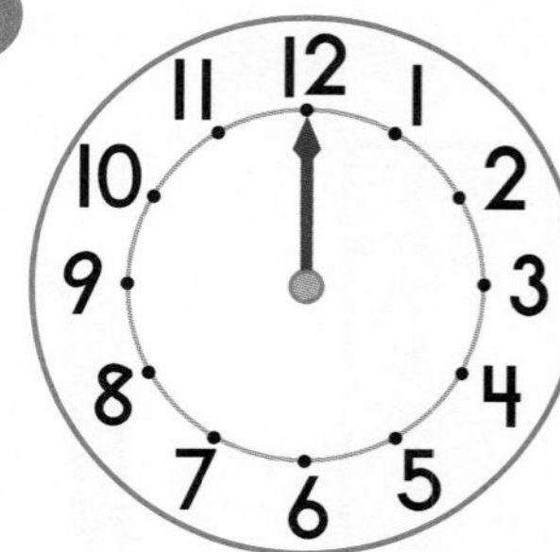

5:00

Dear Family: Discuss a family activity that takes place at a certain time. When you begin the activity, look at a clock and ask your child if you're on time.

Name ______________________________

Cups, Pints, and Quarts

Color the same amount.

1

4

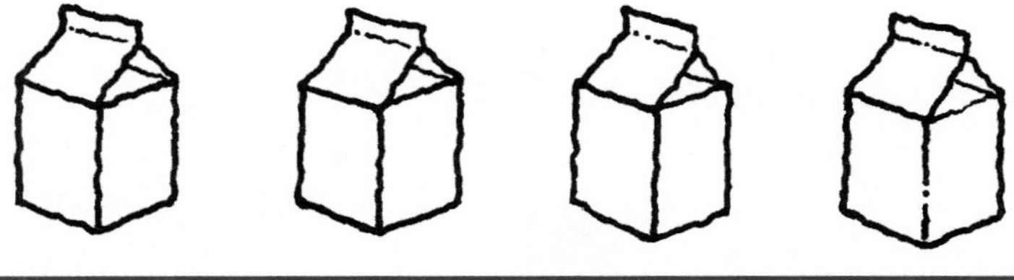

5

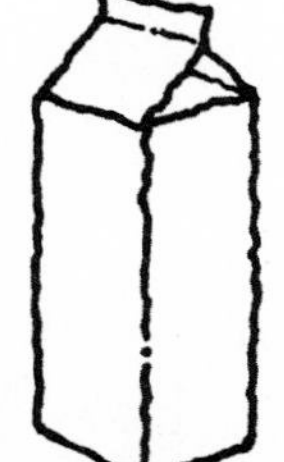

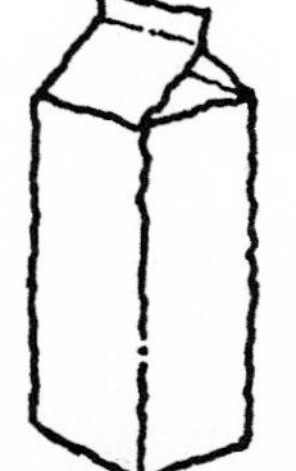

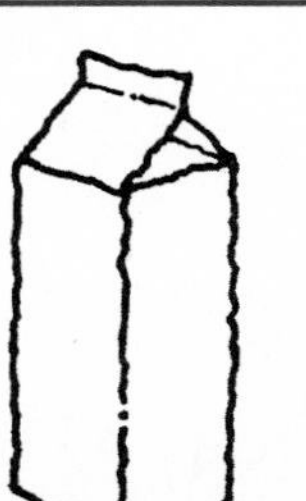

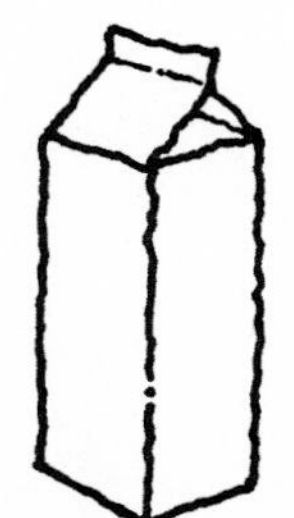

6 Ring containers that hold more than a quart.

7 Ring containers that hold less than a quart.

Dear Family: Find containers that measure quarts, pints, and cups in your home. Have your child show you how quarts, pints, and cups are related.

Name ______________________________

Measure It

1. Listen.

2. The can weighs one pound.
Ring the food that weighs more than one pound.

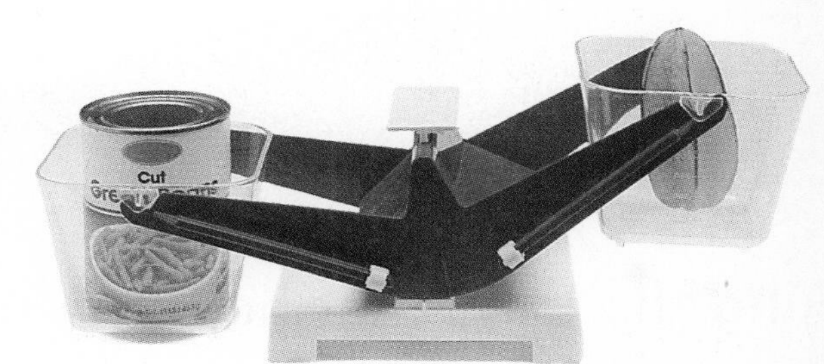
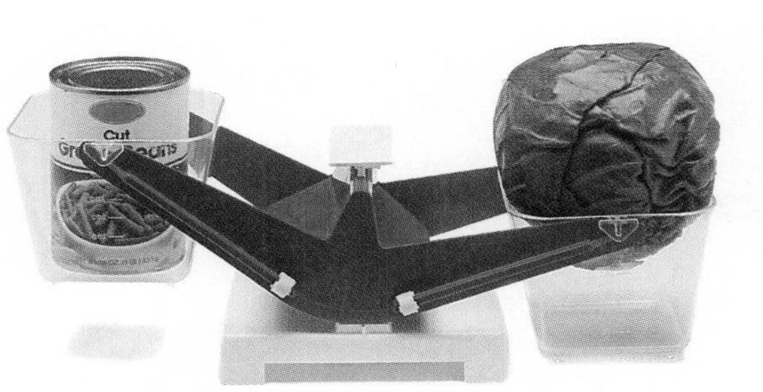

3. Draw something that weighs more than one pound.

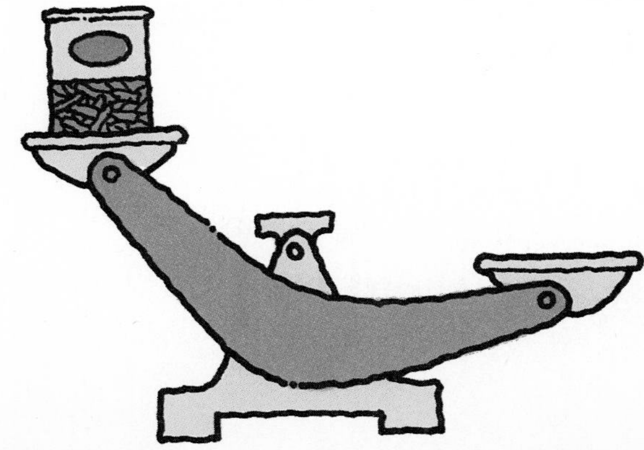

Measure. Then write the length.

4

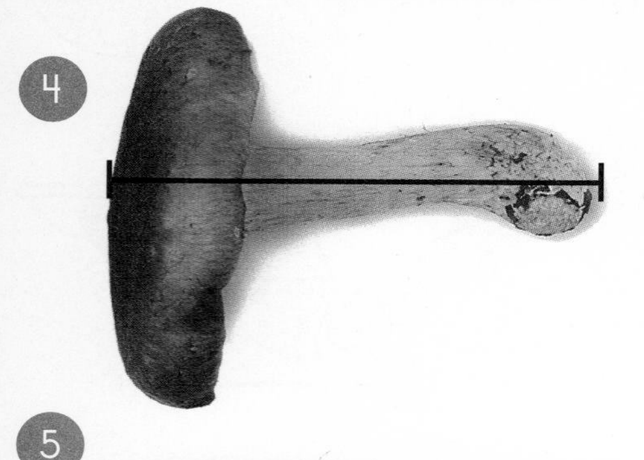

_____ inches

5

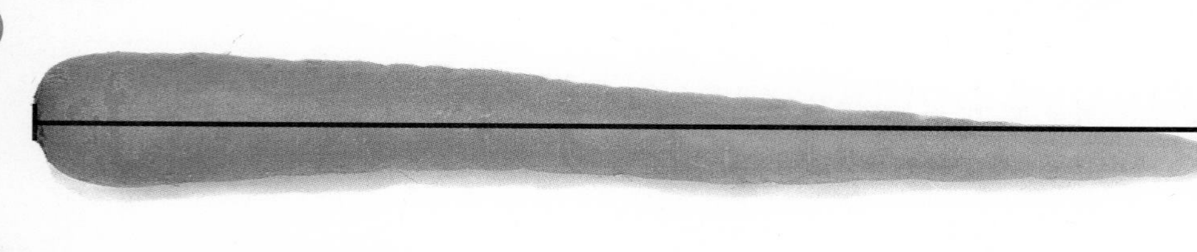

_____ inches

6

_____ inches

Ring the trays that hold the same amount as a quart.

7

Dear Family: Ask your child to show you how to measure in inches. Suggest measuring different objects around your home.

Name ______________________________

Moving On to New Facts

Draw a line to connect the addition and subtraction problems. Write the difference.

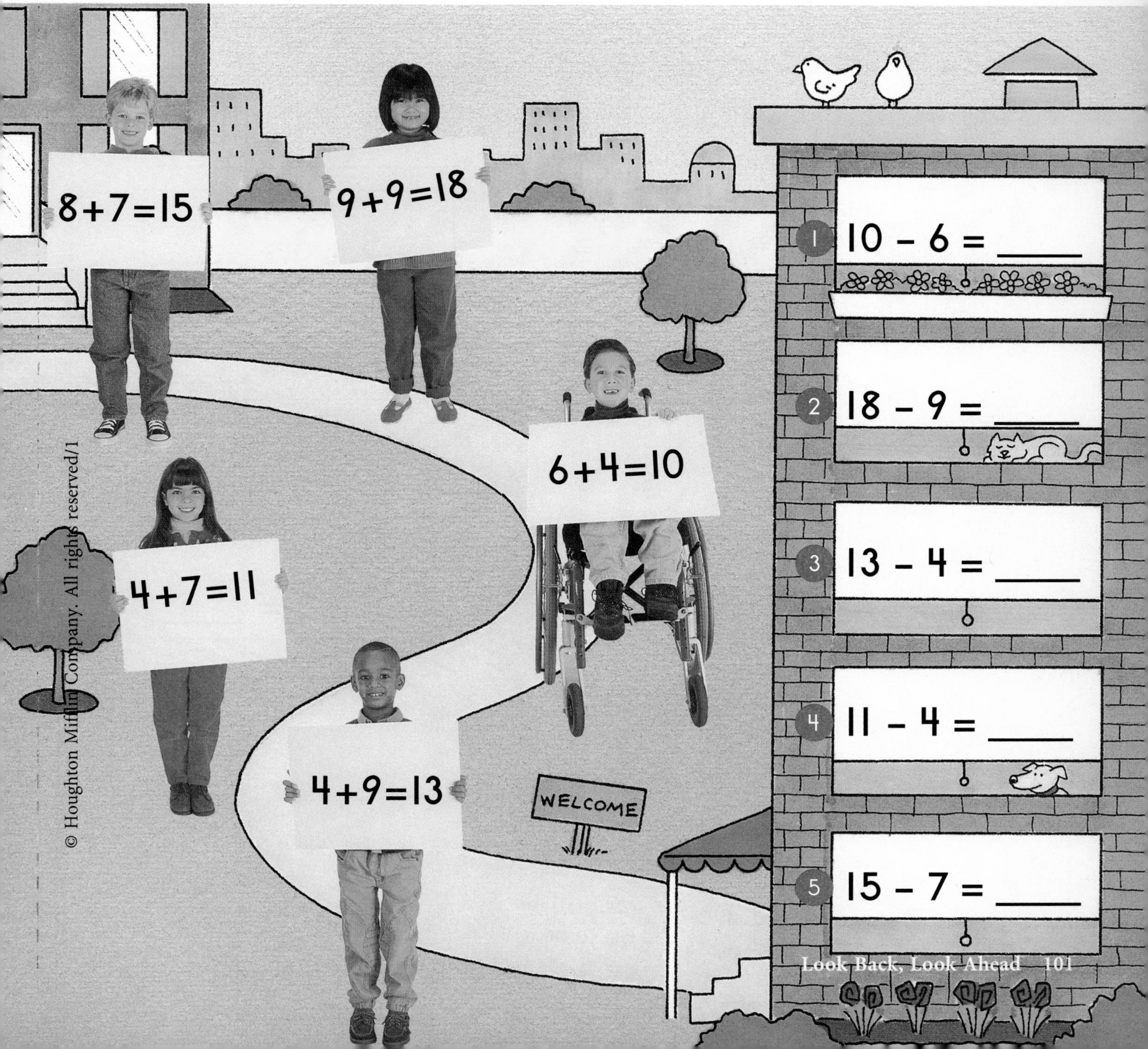

8+7=15

9+9=18

6+4=10

4+7=11

4+9=13

WELCOME

1 10 − 6 = ____

2 18 − 9 = ____

3 13 − 4 = ____

4 11 − 4 = ____

5 15 − 7 = ____

Find the domino that helps you solve the addition problem. Draw a line to connect. Write the sum.

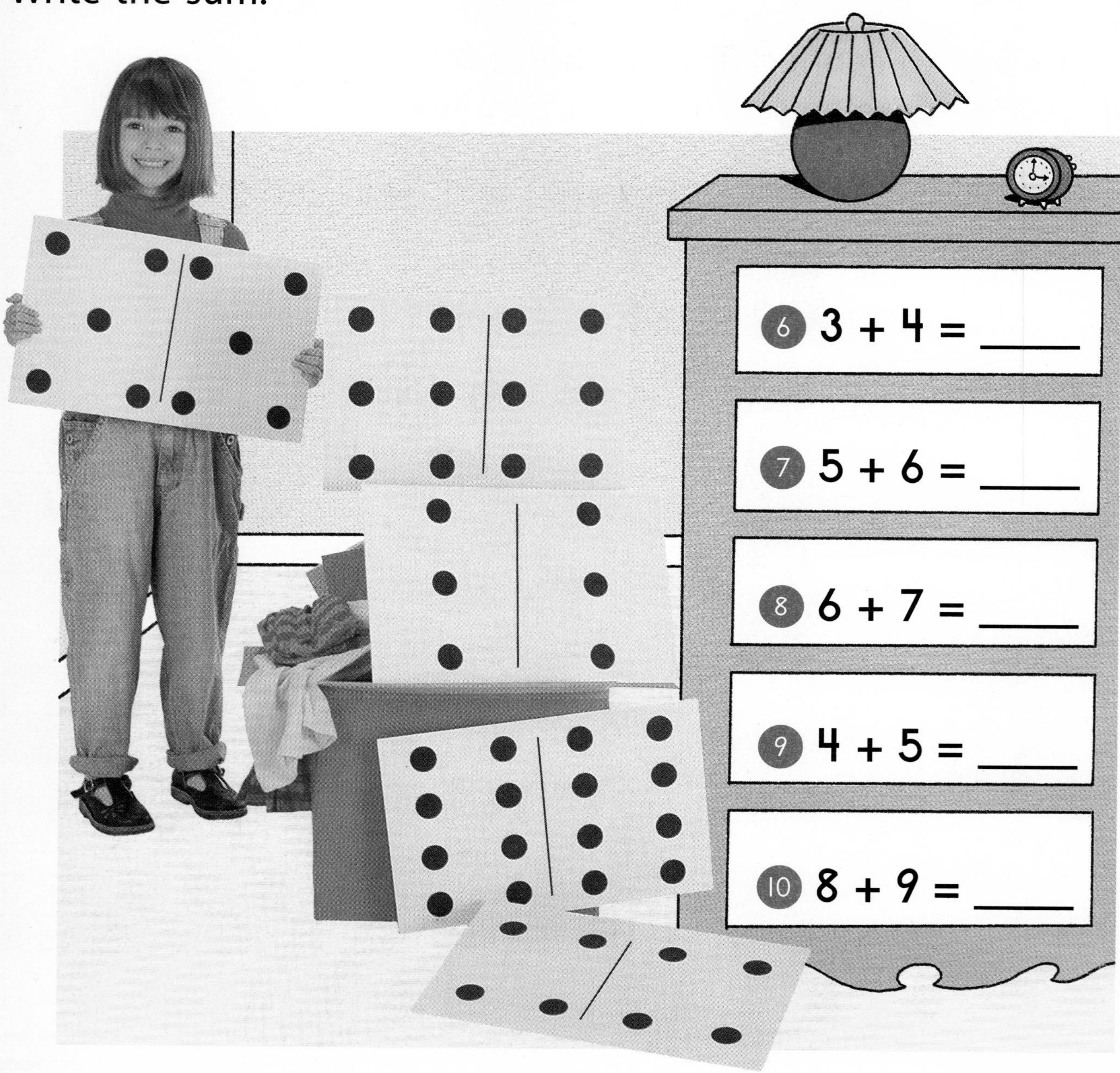

Dear Family: Gather 18 small objects. Help your child separate some of them into two groups and say the addition fact. Repeat with other groups.

Name ______________________________

How Many and How Old?

1. Ring tens to count the chairs.

Model the story using blocks.
Write the number sentence.

2. ____ ◯ ____ = ____

3. ____ ◯ ____ = ____

4. ____ ◯ ____ = ____

5. ____ ◯ ____ = ____

What is the correct age? Ring your estimate.

10

I am 88. 8 years ago I was...

105 80 46

11

I am 6. In 50 years I will be...

65 56 46

Dear Family: Work with your child to determine what age each household member will be when your child turns 10.

Name ________________________________

How Does Your Garden Grow?

Draw to continue the patterns.
Write the number for each step.

1

_____ _____ _____ _____ _____

2

_____ _____ _____ _____ _____

3

_____ _____ _____ _____ _____

4

_____ _____ _____ _____ _____

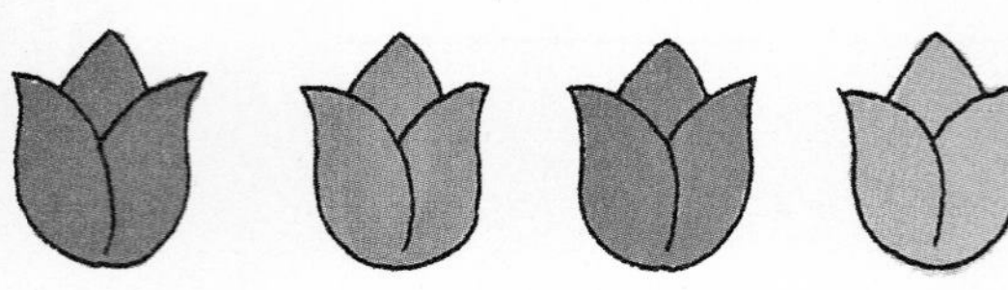

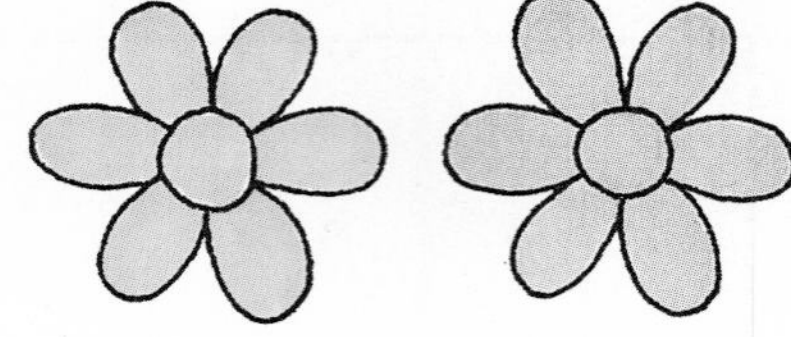

5 Color all the ways you can combine one tulip and one daisy.

Dear Family: Choose 3 pairs of pants and 3 shirts and have your child help you figure out how many ways you can combine them.

Picture Glossary

Data

tallies

bar graph

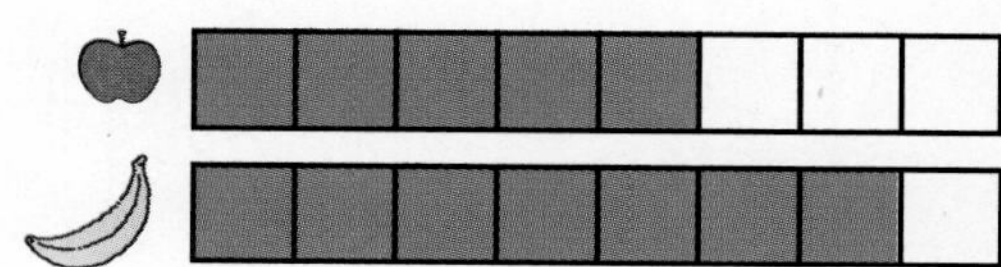

Number

greater than

15 > 9

15 is greater than 9

less than

7 < 14

7 is less than 14

one half

$\frac{1}{2}$

one third

$\frac{1}{3}$

one fourth

$\frac{1}{4}$ 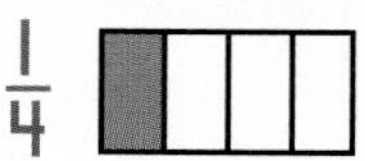

Computation

addition

plus sign, sum

7 + 2 = 9

addends, equal sign

subtraction

minus sign

10 − 6 = 4

difference

Geometry

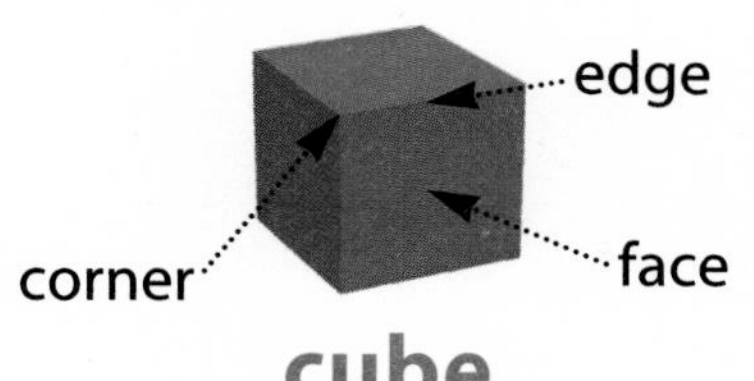

cube

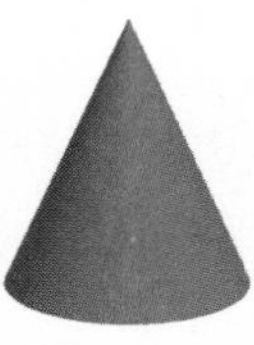

cone

sphere

cylinder

square

circle

triangle

rectangle

Measurement

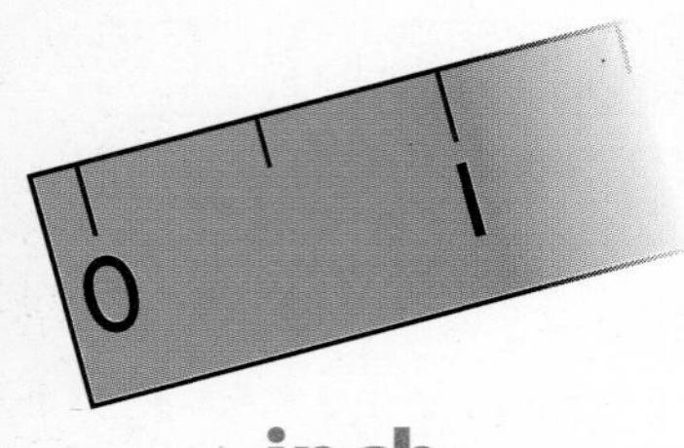

inch

pound

cup

pint

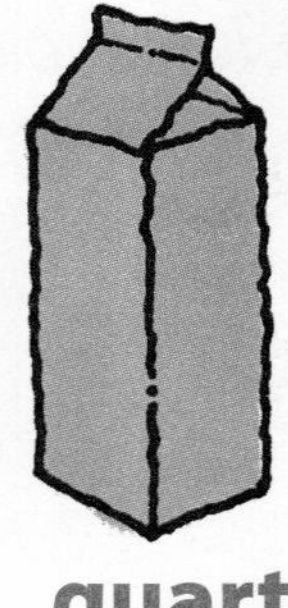
quart

centimeter

kilogram

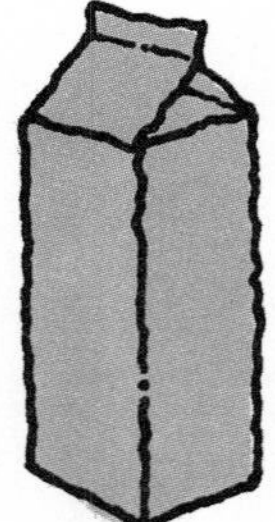
liter

penny

nickel

dime

quarter

dollar

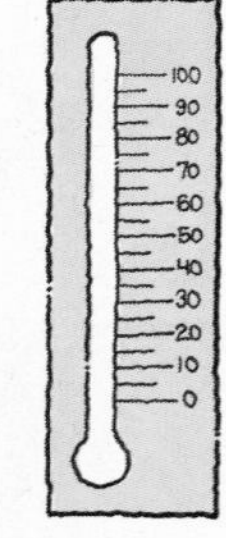

thermometer

ruler

scale

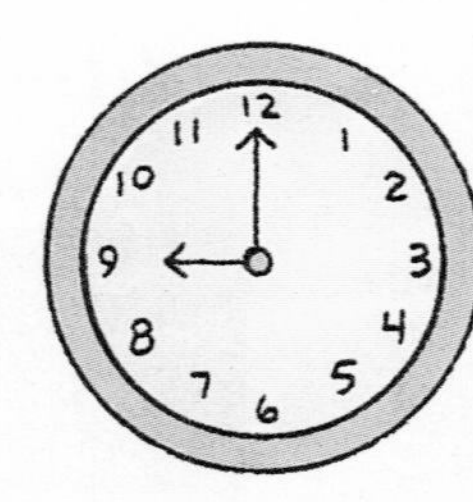

clock